100 SCIENCE HOMEWORK ACTIVITIES

Introduction

Reference grid

Homework diar

Teachers' notes   page 9

Homework activities   page 28

Published by
Scholastic Ltd,
Villiers House,
Clarendon Avenue,
Leamington Spa,
Warwickshire CV32 5PR

Printed by Ebenezer Baylis and Son Ltd, Worcester

© Scholastic Ltd 2002
Text © Malcolm Anderson and David
Tomlinson
1 2 3 4 5 6 7 8 9 0 2 3 4 5 6 7 8 9 0 1

Authors
Malcolm Anderson (Year 3) and David Tomlinson (Year 4)

Editor
Joel Lane

Assistant Editor
Clare Gallaher

Series Designer
Micky Pledge

Cover photography
Martyn Chillmaid

Illustrations
Peter Stevenson (Year 3) and Tim Archbold (Year 4)

Acknowledgements
The National Curriculum for England 2000
© The Queens Printer and Controller of HMSO. Reproduced under the terms of HMSO Guidance Note 8.
A Scheme of Work for Key Stages 1 and 2: Science
© Qualifications and Curriculum Authority. Reproduced under the terms of HMSO Guidance Note 8.

British Library Cataloguing-in-Publication Data
A catalogue record for this book is available from the British Library.

ISBN 0-590-53724-5

The right of David Tomlinson and Malcolm Anderson to be identified as the Author of this work has been asserted by them in accordance with the Copyright, Designs and Patents Act 1988.

Teachers should consult their own school policies and guidelines concerning practical work and participation of children in science experiments. You should only select activities which you feel can be carried out safely and confidently in the classroom.

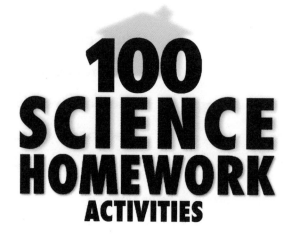

100 SCIENCE HOMEWORK ACTIVITIES

100 Science Homework Activities is a series of resource books for teachers of Years 1–6 (Scottish Primary 1–7). Each book of 100 activities covers two year groups, with around 50 activities specific to each year. These provide a 'core' of homework tasks in line with the National Curriculum documents for science in England, Wales and Northern Ireland and, in England, the QCA's *Science Scheme of Work*. The tasks also meet the requirements of the 5–14 National Guidelines for science in Scotland.

The homework activities are intended as a support for all science teachers, be they school science leader or trainee teacher. They can be used with any science scheme of work as the basis for planning homework activities throughout the school in line with your homework policy. If you are using the companion series, *100 Science Lessons*, these books are designed to complement the lesson plans in the corresponding year's book. Activities can be used with single- or mixed-age classes, single- and mixed-ability groups, and for team planning of homework across a year or key stage. You may also find the activities valuable for extension work in class, or as additional resources.

Using the books

100 Science Homework Activities has been planned to offer a range of simple science exercises for children to carry out at home. Many are designed for sharing with a helper, who could be a parent or carer, another adult in the family, an older sibling, or a neighbour. They include a variety of games, puzzles, observations and practical investigations, each of which has been chosen to ensure complete coverage of all UK national curricula for science.

Teacher support

There are supporting teachers' notes for each of the 100 activities in this book, briefly outlining the following:

Learning objectives: the specific learning objectives that the homework aims to address, based on the four curriculum documents, and linked to the same learning objectives from the relevant *100 Science Lessons* book.

Lesson context: a brief description of the classroom experience recommended for the children before undertaking the homework activity.

Setting the homework: advice on how to explain the worksheet to the children, and how to set it in context before it is taken home.

Back at school: suggestions for how to respond to the completed homework, including discussion with the children or specific advice on marking, as well as answers where relevant.

Photocopiable pages

Each of the 100 homework activities in this book includes a photocopiable worksheet for children to take home. The page provides instructions for the child and a brief explanation of the task for the helper, stating simply and clearly the activity's purpose and suggesting ideas for support or a further challenge to offer the child. The science topic addressed by each activity, and the type of homework being offered, are both indicated at the top of each page. There are seven types of homework activity:

Science to share activities encourage the child, with their helper, to talk and work together on a science task. These tasks draw heavily on things likely to be found at home.

Science practice/revision activities are tasks designed to reinforce knowledge or understanding gained during lesson time.

Numeracy/Literacy link activities practise skills from other areas of the curriculum within a science context.

Finding out activities are designed to increase children's knowledge through investigations, keeping diaries, or by consulting simple secondary sources.

 Observation tasks require children to look closely and carefully at things around the home to gain more detailed knowledge of a science topic.

 Ask an adult activities help children to understand that asking questions is a valuable way of finding out more about a particular subject, particularly when they are too young to have experienced a particular activity or event themselves.

The grids on pages 4–7 provide an overview of the book's content, showing how each activity can be matched to the curriculum: in England to the National Curriculum for science and the QCA *Science Scheme of Work,* and in Scotland to the 5–14 National Guidelines.

Using these activities with the *100 Science Lessons* series

The organisation of the homework activities in this book matches that of the activities in *100 Science Lessons: Year 3* (written by Malcolm Anderson) and *Year 4* (written by Kendra McMahon), both published by Scholastic, so that there are homework activities matching the learning objectives in each unit of work. The grids on pages 4–7 in this book show which lessons in *100 Science Lessons: Year 3* and *Year 4* have associated homework activities here, together with the relevant page numbers from the main books to help with planning.

Supporting your helpers

As well as the notes on each of the worksheets, there is a photocopiable homework diary – provided on page 8 – which can be sent home with each of the homework activities. The diary has space for recording four pieces of homework, and multiple copies can be stapled together to make a longer-term homework record. There is space to record the activity's title and the date it was sent home, and spaces for responses to the homework from the child, the helper and your own comment. The diary is intended to encourage home–school links, so that parents or carers know what is being taught and can make informed comments about their child's progress.

About this book: Years 3&4/ Primary 4–5

This book provides 100 creative science homework activities for seven- to nine-year-olds. Each unit offers six or seven activities to support a topic, so even if you choose not to use all the activities as homework there is plenty of

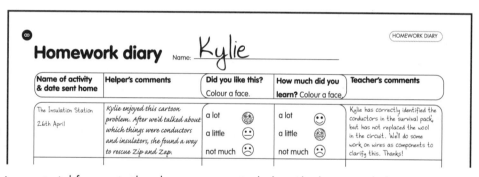

choice, and a wealth of extension material for use in the classroom, particularly with classroom helpers.

All areas of the National Curriculum are covered in this book. Activities on space and energy have been included to meet Scottish requirements, and to support teachers elsewhere who are not following the QCA *Science Scheme of Work.* Although the activities in both halves of the book cover similar content, those for Year 4/Primary 5 build on those for the previous year, and are generally more demanding, not only in terms of scientific understanding but also in terms of literacy and numeracy. In Years 3 & 4/Primary 4–5, children will still be at different stages of reading and writing, so you will need to make it clear to helpers that they should read the instructions with the children and, if necessary, help them with their writing.

For children in Year 3/Primary 4, science is all about furthering their curiosity and experience. It is also about consolidating learning from Key Stage 1/Primary 1–3, and beginning to develop some independence and autonomy in planning and carrying out scientific investigations. The majority of the activities need no special resources: they use only simple household equipment or things that are commonly available at home. Many encourage the children to make use of their local environment, or to draw on experience of their surroundings; adult supervision is clearly essential for this work.

Key science skills such as predicting, observing, recording and drawing conclusions are central to the Year 4/Primary 5 activities. Quantitative science truly begins here. Most of the activities also emphasise practical participation, affording the children opportunities to try things out for themselves and to put their discoveries into a scientific context. Links between school science lessons and the home setting are made throughout these activities by putting characters that the children can relate to into familiar situations, so that the children begin to see and question the science around them. The aim is to harness the children's natural curiosity about their world, and to give them the tools to express themselves in a structured form that will support their progress at school.

Page in this book	Activity name	Homework type	Learning objectives	QCA Unit	National Curriculum	Scottish 5–14 Guidelines	Unit	Lesson	Page
28	Healthy eating	Science to share	To realise that food can be put into different groups.	3A	Sc2 2b	Developing informed attitudes	1	2	13
29	Health food café	Numeracy link	To know that a knowledge of food groups helps us to build healthy diets.	3A	Sc2 2b	Developing informed attitudes	1	4	16
30	Growing up	Literacy link	To know that humans grow.	3A	Sc2 2f	Living things & the processes of life – B	1	5	18
31	Amazing teeth	Finding out	To know the different types of teeth and their functions.	3A	Sc2 2b	Developing informed attitudes	1	6	19
32	Taking care of teeth	Science practice	To know that teeth and gums need care to stay healthy.	3A	Sc2	Developing informed attitudes	1	8	21
33	Making sense	Science practice	To know that the senses make us aware of our surroundings.	3A	Sc1 1f	The processes of life – B	1	9	22
34	Mr Fergs' wordsearch	Science practice	To know that there are certain processes which can be used to identify a living thing	3B	Sc2 1a	The processes of life – C	2	2	36
35	Movement survey	Numeracy link	To know that different animals move in different ways.	3B	Sc2 2e	The processes of life – C	2	3	38
36	Animal senses	Science practice	To know that animals have senses that make them aware of their surroundings.	3B	Sc2 1a, 2e	The processes of life – B	2	4	39
37	Little and large	Literacy link	To know that animals grow and reproduce.	3B	Sc2 1a	The processes of life – C	2	5	41
38	Food from plants	Finding out	To know that most of our diet comes from plants.	3B	Sc2 2b	The processes of life – C	2	9	45
39	Looking at roots	Observation	To know that the roots take up water and anchor the plant to the ground.	3B	Sc2 3a, 3c	The processes of life – B & C	2	11	47
40	At the garden centre	Science to share	To know that different plants prefer different places in which to grow.	3B	Sc2 5b	The processes of life – C	2	14	49
41	World environments	Science practice	To know that the world environment can be divided into parts.	–	Sc2 5b	The processes of life – B	3	4	71
42	Voyage of discovery	Literacy link	To know that the climate affects where plants and animals live.	–	Sc2 5b	The processes of life – C	3	5	72
43	Who lives there?	Finding out	To know that the climate affects where plants and animals live.	–	Sc2 5b	The processes of life – C	3	5	72
44	Habitats	Science practice	To know that living things in a habitat are affected by light and shade, dryness and moisture, heat and cold	–	Sc2 5b	The processes of life – C	3	6	74
45	How much waste?	Numeracy link	To know that there are many waste products that can affect the environment.	–	Sc2 5a	The processes of life – C	3	9	76
46	Don't waste it, recycle it!	Science practice	To know that there are many waste products that can affect the environment.	–	Sc2 5a	The processes of life – C	3	9	76
47	Inside my house	Science practice	To know a range of common materials and that some materials may have different uses.	3C	Sc3 1a	Materials from Earth – B	4	2	88
48	Now and then	Ask an adult	To know a range of common materials and that a material may have different uses.	3C	Sc3 1a	Materials from Earth – B	4	2	88
49	Material adjectives	Literacy link	To know that any material may have more than one property.	3C	Sc3 1a	Materials from Earth – B	4	3	89
50	Natural or manufactured?	Finding out	To know that some materials occur naturally and others do not.	3C	Sc3 1a	Materials from Earth – B	4	7	94
51	Rocks	Numeracy link	To be able to recognise and describe a range of different rocks.	3D	Sc3 1d	Materials from Earth – B	4	9	96
52	Soil	Science to share	To know there are different kinds of soil.	3C	Sc3 1d	Materials from Earth – B	4	12	98

Page in this book	Activity name	Homework type	Learning objectives	QCA Unit	National Curriculum	Scottish 5–14 Guidelines	Unit	Lesson	Page
53	There's a fault here!	Science to share	To know that electricity can be dangerous and must be treated with great care.	–	Sc4 1a	Properties & uses of energy – C	5	2	114
54	Writing instructions	Literacy link	To know how to make a simple circuit with a switch.	–	Sc4 1a	–	5	3	116
55	Broken circuits	Science practice	To identify circuits that will not let electricity flow.	–	Sc4 1a	Properties & uses of energy – C	5	4	117
56	Morse code	Science to share	To know that electricity is used for communicating with sound (light).	–	Sc4 1a	Properties & uses of energy – C	5	7	120
57	Communication survey	Finding out	To know that electricity is used for communication systems.	–	Sc4 1a	Properties & uses of energy – C	5	8	122
58	What's on the TV?	Numeracy link	To know that electricity is used for communication systems.	–	Sc4 1a	Properties & uses of energy – C	5	8	122
59	Push or pull?	Science practice	To know there are forces between magnets which push and pull.	3E	Sc4 2a	Forces and their effects – B	6	2	132
60	The Great Magnet Game	Science practice	To know that some materials are magnetic and others are not.	3E	Sc4 2a	Forces and their effects – B	6	3	134
61	Jack in the Box	Science to share	To know that springs and elastic bands exert forces.	3E	Sc4 2d	–	6	6	138
62	Stretchy elastic	Science to share	To know that the force exerted by an elastic band depends on how much it is stretched.	3E	Sc4 2e	Forces and their effects – B	6	9	141
63	Vehicle building	Literacy link	To know that energy can change forms.	3E	Sc4 2d	Conversion & transfer of energy – B	6	11	143
64	Energy and fuel	Finding out	To know that heat is a form of energy and it may be supplied by several sources. To know that energy can change forms.	3E	Sc1 1l	Conversion & transfer of energy – C	6	12	144
65	Me and my shadow	Literacy link	To know that when light from the Sun is blocked by an object, a shadow forms.	3F	Sc4 3b	Properties & uses of energy – C	7	2	156
66	Light sources	Science practice	To know that when light from sources other than the Sun is blocked, shadows are also produced.	3F	Sc4 3b	Properties & uses of energy – C	7	3	158
67	Car colour survey	Numeracy link	To know that colours are used for decoration and to give messages in the man-made world.	3F	Sc4 3d	Properties & uses of energy – B	7	7	161
68	Musical instruments	Finding out	To know that there is a wide variety of sound sources.	3F	Sc4 3e	Properties & uses of energy – B	7	9	164
69	Making music	Science practice	To know that of the many sounds around us at any one time some are loud, some are soft/quiet, some are high- and others are low-pitched.	3F	Sc4 3f	Properties & uses of energy – B	7	11	166
70	Sound words	Literacy link	To know about some of the uses of sound.	3F	Sc4 3e, 3g	Properties & uses of energy – B	7	13	167
71	Shadow puppets	Science to share	To know that shadows are formed when objects block light from the Sun.	3F	Sc4 4b	Properties & uses of energy – B & C	8	2	180
72	Shadow lengths	Numeracy link	To know that the shape and position of a shadow change at different times of day. To be able to measure in standard measures and present results in tables and bar charts.	3F	Sc4 4b	Properties & uses of energy – B & C	8	4	182
73	The Sun in the sky	Science practice	To know that the Sun appears to follow a curved path across the sky every day.	3F	Sc4 4b	Properties & uses of energy – B & C	8	5	183
74	The Sun	Finding out	To understand that the Sun is at the centre of the Solar System and the Earth orbits it.	3F	Sc4 4c, 4d	Earth & Space – C; Properties & uses of energy – B	8	7	185
75	The Solar System	Literacy link	To understand that the Sun is at the centre of the Solar System and the Earth orbits it.	3F	Sc4 4c, 4d	Earth & Space – B; Properties & uses of energy – B & C	8	7	185
76	Sundials	Finding out	To know that shadows can be used to tell the approximate time of day.	3F	Sc4 4b		8	8	187

REFERENCE GRID YEAR 4

Page in this book	Activity name	Homework type	Learning objectives	QCA Unit	National Curriculum	Scottish 5–14 Guidelines	Unit	Lesson	Page
77	X-ray observation	Science practice	To know that the skeleton is made from bones. To know that we have many joined bones to give a greater range of movement.	4A	Sc1 1a; Sc2 2e, 2f	The processes of life – C; Reviewing and reporting on tasks/Carrying out tasks – B	1	2	13
78	Growing Gallery	Science to share	To know that a skeleton grows from birth to adulthood.	4A	Sc1 1b, 2b; Sc2 2e, 2f	The processes of life – B & C; Preparing for tasks – B; Carrying out tasks – B	1	3	14
79	Dr Dreadful's disaster	Science practice	To know that the skeleton supports and protects organs in the body. To locate and name some organs of the body.	–	Sc1 2h; Sc2 2e	The processes of life – C	1	6	17
80	Top of the hops	Numeracy link	To know that the action of muscles helps the body to move. To observe their own bodies closely.	4A	Sc1 2l; Sc2 2e	Processes of life – C; Reviewing and reporting on tasks – B	1	7	19
81	Workout	Numeracy link	To know that when muscles work hard in exercise they also affect the body in other ways.	4A	Sc2 2e	Processes of life – C; Carrying out tasks – B	1	8	21
82	Frazzle a friend!	Finding out	To assess the children's knowledge and understanding of the skeletal system.	4A	Sc1 2b; Sc2 2e	Preparing for tasks – C	1	9	21
83	Sort and Snap	Science to share	To understand that a wide range of living things can be classified as plants or as animals.	–	Sc2 4b	Variety and characteristic features – C	2	1	28
84	Midnight at the House of Doom!	Literacy link	To know that bones have features that can be compared.	4A	Sc1 1a; Sc2 2e	Reviewing and reporting on tasks – D	2	2	29
85	Inside story	Science practice	To recognise similarities and differences between different groups of vertebrates.	4A	Sc1 2l; Sc2 2e	Variety and characteristic features – B & C	2	4	31
86	Take care!	Finding out	To know how to collect animals sensitively.	4A	Sc2 5a	Respect and care: environmental responsibility – C	2	7	34
87	Guests at the House of Doom	Science practice	To know how a decision tree can be used to classify.	–	Sc2 4a	Variety and characteristic features – E	2	8	35
88	Sort it out!	Numeracy link	To assess the children's knowledge of the kinds of skeletons animals have and of the way animals are classified.	4A	Sc2 2e	Variety and characteristic features – B & C	2	9	37
89	My scrapbook	Literacy link	To elicit children's ideas about living things. To know that there is a wide variety of organisms on the planet.	4B	Sc1 2i; Sc2 4b	Variety and characteristic features – A; The processes of life – C	3	1	49
90	Miss Harvey's habitat	Numeracy link	To investigate the plants found in a certain habitat. To compare the numbers of different types of plants in two habitats.	4B	Sc1 2h; Sc2 5b	Interaction – C; Carrying out tasks – B	3	5	54
91	Ideal Homes Exhibition	Science practice	To begin to explore the relationships between the physical aspects and the plants and animals living in a habitat.	4B	Sc2 5b, 5c	Skills in science – D; Interaction – D	3	6	56
92	What's for dinner?	Science practice	To understand what is meant by a food chain. To know what the words *producer* and *consumer* mean.	4B	Sc2 5d	Interaction of living things with their environment – B	3	11	61
93	What's cooking?	Science to share	To understand the terms *herbivore* and *carnivore*. To understand that food chains are part of more complex food webs.	4B	Sc1 2c; Sc2 5d, 5e	Interaction of living things with their environment – B	3	13	63
94	Dinner for two?	Science practice	To understand the terms *herbivore* and *carnivore*. To understand that food chains are part of more complex food webs.	4B	Sc1 2c; Sc2 5d, 5e	Interaction of living things with their environment – B	3	13	63
95	Disappearing aliens	Science practice	To know that camouflage helps some animals to survive.	4B	Sc1 2c	Interaction of living things with their environment – D	3	14	64
96	Park life	Science practice	To know that seasonal changes influence animals and plants in a habitat. To know that nature changes habitats.	4B	Sc2 1c	Earth in space – B; Interaction of living things with their environment – A, D	3	16	66
97	Material world	Science practice	To elicit children's existing understanding about materials.	4D	Sc3 1a	Reviewing and reporting on tasks – B; Materials from Earth – B	4	1	81
98	Where in the world?	Numeracy link	To know that a thermometer is an instrument for measuring temperature. To measure in standard units with appropriate accuracy.	4C	Sc1 2i; Sc3 2c	Carrying out tasks – B	4	2	83
99	Blake's temperature trauma	Numeracy link	To describe and suggest explanations for temperature findings.	4C	Sc1 2g, 2h; Sc3 2c	Reviewing and reporting on tasks – C	4	3	84
100	The revenge of Doctor Chill	Literacy link	To know that the heat insulation property of materials can be compared by investigation.	4C 4D	Sc3 2b	Changing materials – B; Materials from Earth – C	4	4	85
101	At home with Zip and Zap	Science practice	To know that some materials can be classified as solids and some as liquids. To describe some of the properties of solids and liquids.	4D	Sc1 2l; Sc3 1e	Materials from Earth C	4	8	90

Page in this book	Activity name	Homework type	Learning objectives	QCA Unit	National Curriculum	Scottish 5–14 Guidelines	Unit	Lesson	Page
102	Jelly journal	Science to share	To know that a solid can be changed into a liquid by melting and a liquid into a solid by freezing.	4D	Sc1 2e, 2f, 2h, 2i, 2j; Sc3 1e, 2b, 2d	Reviewing and reporting on tasks – D; Changing materials – B	4	12	94
103	Light me!	Science revision	To review work on electricity from Y3/P4, including the idea that a complete circuit is needed for a device to work.	4F	Sc4 1a, 1c;	Properties and uses of energy – C	5	1	111
104	Batteries or mains?	Science revision	As for 'Light me!' above.	4F	Sc1 2h; Sc4 1a	Properties and uses of energy – C	5	2	113
105	Delivery day	Science practice	To know that mains electricity is a form of energy that has been converted from other forms of energy.	4F	Sc1 2b	Properties and uses of energy – D	5	3	113
106	The Insulation Station	Literacy link	To know that electricity flows through some materials and not others.	4F	Sc4 1c	Properties and uses of energy – D	5	4	114
107	Circus circuits	Science to share	To know that batteries may be connected together to give greater electrical power.	4F	Sc4 1a, 1b	Properties and uses of energy – C	5	8	118
108	Stand back, Zip and Zap!	Literacy link	To communicate ideas about electricity.	4F	Sc4 1a	Properties and uses of energy – C	5	10	122
109	Push, pull or twist dominoes	Science to share	To know that a force acts in a particular direction and this can be represented by an arrow.	4E	KS1 Sc4 2b, 2c; KS2 Sc4 2d	Forces and their effects – B	6	1	132
110	Sian's speedy skittles 1	Science practice	To know that friction is a force. To know that friction depends on the surfaces in contact.	4E	Sc1 2c; Sc4 2c	Carrying out tasks – D	6	5	136
111	Friction Rollerball	Numeracy link	To know that the force of friction depends on the surfaces in contact.	4E	Sc 1 2d, 2j; Sc4 2c	Preparing for tasks – B	6	6	138
112	Force report	Literacy link	To introduce the term gravity as the force that pulls things down.	4E	Sc1 1a; Sc4 2b, 2c	Reviewing and reporting on tasks – D	6	10	142
113	A game of two forces	Science to share	To know that air resistance can slow down the movement of objects. To know that a force acts in a direction that can be represented by an arrow.	4E	Sc1 2e; Sc4 2c	Forces and their effects – C	6	11	142
114	Sian's speedy skittles 2	Numeracy link	To present data in the form of a bar chart.	4E	Sc1 2e, 2f, 2h; Sc4 2c	Carrying out tasks – C	6	12	144
115	Disappearing tricks	Literacy link	To assess the children's understanding of how forces can affect the shape and movement of objects.	4E	Sc4 2b,c; Breadth of study 2a	Forces and their effects – B, C	6	13	145
116	Trapped in the House of Doom!	Science to share	To understand that the position of a shadow depends on the direction of the light source.	–	Sc4 3b	Properties and uses of energy – C	7	3	159
118	How light travels	Science practice	To know that rays are reflected from surfaces.	–	Sc1 2c; Sc4 3c	Properties and uses of energy – C	7	6	162
119	Wake up, Grandma!	Numeracy link	To help children make connections with previous work on sound.	–	Sc1 2h; Sc4 3e, 3f	Properties and uses of energy – C	7	7	162
120	Which pitch?	Science practice	To recognise high and low pitch, and that the pitch of a sound is related to the size of the vibrating part of an object.	–	Sc1 2j; Sc4 3e, 3f	Properties and uses of energy – C, D	7	9	165
121	Cool vibes!	Science practice	To know that a larger vibrating body makes a louder sound.	–	Sc1 2k; Sc4 3f	Preparing for tasks – C; Properties and uses of energy – C, D	7	11	167
122	The sound of poetry	Literacy link	To apply knowledge and understanding of sound gained in previous lessons.	–	Sc1 1a	Properties and uses of energy – C	7	12	169
123	Planet file	Finding out	To elicit children's existing ideas about Earth and space.	–	Sc1 2b	Earth in space – C	8	1	181
124	Escape from the StarTrap!	Numeracy link	To use a compass to find north, south, east, west and mid-points between them, for example north-east.	–	Sc1 1j	Carrying out tasks – C	8	2	182
125	Sunset diary	Literacy link	To track the apparent movement of the Sun across the sky during the day.	–	Sc1 2f; Sc4 4b	Reviewing and reporting on tasks – D; Earth in Space – B, C	8	3	183
126	Shady days at the House of Doom	Numeracy link	To investigate how shadows change when the angle of the Sun changes.	–	Sc4 4b	Carrying out tasks – C; Properties and uses of energy – C	8	4	184
127	Here comes the Sun	Science practice	To know that the way the Sun heats the Earth depends on the slant of the Sun's rays. To measure temperature.	–	Sc1 1i, 1j; Sc4 4c, 4d	Earth in Space – B; Properties and uses of energy – B, C	8	5	185
128	Crazy Constellations	Science to share	To know what constellations are. To be able to identify some constellations.	–	Sc1 1e	Earth in Space – C, E	8	7	187

Homework diary

Name: _____

Name of activity & date sent home	Helper's comments	Did you like this? Colour a face.	How much did you learn? Colour a face	Teacher's comments
		a lot 😊 a little 😐 not much ☹️	a lot 😊 a little 😐 not much ☹️	
		a lot 😊 a little 😐 not much ☹️	a lot 😊 a little 😐 not much ☹️	
		a lot 😊 a little 😐 not much ☹️	a lot 😊 a little 😐 not much ☹️	
		a lot 😊 a little 😐 not much ☹️	a lot 😊 a little 😐 not much ☹️	

Teachers' notes

UNIT 1 OURSELVES) TEETH AND FOOD

p28 Healthy eating) SCIENCE TO SHARE

Learning objective
● To realise that food can be put into different groups.

Lesson context
Talk to the children about different types of food. Explain that there are three main food groups: energy-giving foods (good for activity), body-building foods (good for growth) and maintenance foods (which keep us healthy). Sort and label the contents of a shopping bag. Ask the children to design an icon for each food group.

Setting the homework
This activity reinforces the concept of a balanced, healthy diet. Care should be taken not to cause any embarrassment to children whose families are not concerned with eating a healthy diet.

Back at school
Talk about the shopping lists the children have put together. Look for similarities and differences. Encourage the children to begin to draw non-judgemental conclusions, such as 'Most of the shopping lists contain more foods for energy than foods for growth.'

p29 Health food café) NUMERACY LINK

Learning objective
● To know that a knowledge of food groups helps us to build healthy diets.

Lesson context
Talk with the children about the scientific reasons for eating a variety of foods. Explain that different foods have different functions for our bodies. Contrast two sample menus or shopping lists: one healthy, one not.

Setting the homework
This activity develops awareness of healthy eating, and encourages the children to eat healthily when they eat out. It can be supported by referring to your school's cafeteria system for serving school meals.

Back at school
Look for strategies used to calculate the costs of the meals. Recognising and using £.p notation is a key objective for Year 3 in the English NNS. Encourage the children to discuss and share their methods of calculation.

p30 Growing up) LITERACY LINK

Learning objective
● To know that humans grow.

Lesson context
Talk to the children about how they have grown. Look at photographs of people at various life stages, from birth to old age. Discuss what the children observe. Is the rate of growth steady, or are there times of more rapid growth?

Setting the homework
Each child will need the activity sheet as a stimulus to think about and record significant events in his or her life, then write a brief 'autobiography'.

Back at school
Discuss the children's life stories; encourage some to tell their stories to the class. You could compile a class book of autobiographies.

p31 Amazing teeth) FINDING OUT

Learning objective
● To know the different types of teeth and their functions.

Lesson context
Discuss the importance of teeth in digestion, and how we have different types of teeth with different functions. Distribute fruit so the children can observe the functions of the teeth. Ask the children to use mirrors to observe their own teeth and carry out some research into how many teeth of each type people have at various ages.

Setting the homework
This is an extension of the lesson, encouraging the children to find out more about teeth. Where access to resources may be difficult, lend children suitable reference books.

Back at school
Talk about the findings and see who has found the most amazing fact. Make a display to share some of the more surprising facts.

p32 Taking care of teeth) SCIENCE PRACTICE

Learning objective
● To know that teeth and gums need care to stay healthy.

Lesson context
Discuss how and why we should take care of our teeth. Use disclosure tablets to demonstrate the importance of brushing correctly. Carry out a survey of teeth cleaning habits among the class (collect the data anonymously by computer). Ask the children to design a poster promoting dental hygiene.

Setting the homework
Encourage the children to think about their class work as they do the homework, and to remember why they should take care of their teeth. Ask them to consider which of the three children on the sheet is closest to their own dental care routine.

Back at school
Talk about the activity, reinforcing the children's understanding by asking them to explain why it is important for us to care for our teeth in three ways (regular brushing, visiting the dentist, avoiding too much sugary food).

p33 Making sense) SCIENCE PRACTICE

Learning objective
● To know that the senses make us aware of our surroundings.

Lesson context
Encourage the children to talk about how they can identify particular foods by using their senses. Discuss how we use our senses to learn about our surroundings. Ask the children to find out about their sensory organs and what

they tell us. Try a blindfold 'taste testing' of different crisp flavours.

Setting the homework
Remind the children that this activity reinforces their knowledge of the senses and sense organs. Encourage them to think about the work they have just done, and to consider what life would be like without their senses.

Back at school
Encourage the children to share their feelings about the idea of not having particular senses. Some children may have direct experience of blindness or deafness, and this should be treated with appropriate sensitivity.

UNIT 2 ANIMALS & PLANTS | THE NEEDS OF PLANTS AND ANIMALS

p34 Mr Fergs' wordsearch — SCIENCE PRACTICE

Learning objective
● To know that there are certain processes which can be used to identify a living thing.

Lesson context
Discuss how to tell whether something is living or non-living. Ask the children to compare a living pet animal and a stone. Identify the characteristics of living things, and use the mnemonic MR FERGS to reinforce them: Movement, Reproduction, Feeding, Excretion, Respiration, Growth, Sensitivity. (For this age group, consider breathing as respiration rather than as excretion.)

Setting the homework
This activity reinforces the children's understanding of the characteristics of living and non-living things.

Back at school
Check that the children have named the seven life processes and the examples. **Answers:** living – bird, plant, fish, mouse; non-living – wind, book, table, car.

p35 Movement survey — NUMERACY LINK

Learning objective
● To know that different animals move in different ways.

Lesson context
Discuss the ways in which different animals move about. Take the children on a minibeast safari to observe and draw small animals on the move. Back in the classroom, provide resources to help the children find out how different animals move.

Setting the homework
This activity continues the class work. You may need to remind the children how to record their observations using tally marks, and how to create a bar chart. More able children may be able to use a scale with the ratio 1:2.

Back at school
Compile the children's results into one large survey. The data could be entered into a simple database for the children to access.

p36 Animal senses — SCIENCE PRACTICE

Learning objective
● To know that animals have senses that make them aware of their surroundings.

Lesson context
Let the children observe some small pets, such as hamsters or mice. Discuss how the animals learn what is happening around them by using their sense organs. Plan and carry out an investigation to study how the pets use their senses in various situations.

Setting the homework
Talk briefly about the outcomes of the investigation, then explain the homework activity. Remind the children about the five senses and the sensory organs.

Back at school
Check that the children have matched the sensory organs to the animals correctly and identified the senses used.
Crossword answers: 1. nose, 2. eyes, 3. tongue, 4. skin, 5. danger, 6. ears. Hidden word: senses.

p37 Little and large — LITERACY LINK

Learning objective
● To know that animals grow and reproduce.

Lesson context
Talk about human babies and why all plants and animals need to reproduce in order for their species to continue. Use stick insects for an investigation to observe growth over a period of time. Ask the children to identify the adult and infant forms of various animals.

Setting the homework
Introduce the term *diminutive*, meaning (in this context) a word for a young animal. Make sure the children understand that some diminutives are the adult's name with a suffix added, but others are completely different words.

Back at school
Check that the task has been completed correctly and that the children understand what diminutives are. They could be used as a basis for further literacy work, such as sentence construction or spelling. **Answers:** A. 1. cub, 2. chick, 3. kitten, 4. puppy, 5. cub, 6. lamb, 7. calf, 8. child, 9. tadpole, 10. kid; B. 1. duck, 2. spider, 3. owl, 4. pig; C. 1. swan, 2. hare, 3. deer, 4. beetle (or insect).

p38 Food from plants — FINDING OUT

Learning objective
● To know that most of our diet comes from plants.

Lesson context
Guide the children to the idea that all foods come from plants or animals. Together, draw up two lists headed *plants* and *animals* to classify foods by origin. Show how we can trace all the food we eat back (directly or indirectly) to plants. You could introduce the term *food chain*.

Setting the homework
This activity could be completed before the lesson. Make sure that the children can identify foods from plants and foods from animals.

Back at school
Check that the task has been completed correctly. Ask the children to explain their findings, and to draw simple

conclusions about the plant content of their diet (such as the amount of fruit or vegetables they eat). Reinforce the idea that most of our foods come directly from plants.

p39 Looking at roots — OBSERVATION

Learning objective
● To know that the roots take up water and anchor the plant to the ground.

Lesson context
Talk about why we drink water. Display a wilting plant and discuss how a plant takes in water. Let the children examine the root systems of weeds. Put a plant's roots in water in a sealed container and monitor the falling water level.

Setting the homework
Each child will need some dried peas or broad beans and a sheet of blotting paper. If they don't have a jar, a cut-off pop bottle or similar clear container will do. Encourage the children to record their observations daily until the root system is well developed.

Back at school
Discuss the children's observations. Ask what they noticed about the directions in which the root and shoot grew. The root will grow downwards and the shoot upwards regardless of the pea's orientation.

p40 At the garden centre — SCIENCE TO SHARE

Learning objective
● To know that different plants prefer different places in which to grow.

Lesson context
Plan and carry out a survey of wild plants that are growing in contrasting conditions: in a field, under a hedge, on wasteland and so on. Use reference materials to help the children identify some wild plants. Discuss the different conditions they have grown in.

Setting the homework
Remind the children how they found that wild plants tend to 'prefer' certain conditions. The same is true of garden plants, which may have been imported from various different countries. At this stage, it is best to consider weather conditions rather than soil types.

Back at school
Allow the children time to share their findings. Compile a list of plants suited to particular conditions: sunny, shady, dry, damp and so on.

UNIT 3 THE ENVIRONMENT
HOW THE ENVIRONMENT AFFECTS LIVING THINGS

p41 World environments — SCIENCE PRACTICE

Learning objective
● To know that the world environment can be divided into parts.

Lesson context
Ask the children to think about the features of the area where they live. Compare it with a different location, perhaps using the Internet. Discuss the term *environment*. Consider different environments in the world (land, sea and freshwater), and how a major factor that affects an environment is weather. Carry out a local weather study.

Setting the homework
This activity develops the children's understanding of different environments. Encourage them to make sure their descriptions are specific enough to let someone else identify each environment.

Back at school
Check that the contents of the three columns match up. Ask some children to read out their descriptions for the class to identify each environment. You could compile a class description of the four environments.

p42 Voyage of discovery — LITERACY LINK

Learning objective
● To know that the climate affects where plants and animals live.

Lesson context
Discuss the children's weather records from the previous lesson. Ask them what effect the weather has on plants and animals. Discuss migration and how the climate can change during a year. Provide a Carroll diagram (see below) on which the children can identify environments with different characteristics. Let them use secondary sources to find out what plants and animals live in one environment.

	WET		
HOT	Rainforests	Oceans	COLD
	Deserts	Poles	
	DRY		

Setting the homework
The activity focuses on writing a first-person account. Talk about diary entries: how they may be briefer than other styles of writing, but still need to contain enough facts to serve as a record.

Back at school
Read the children's work, looking for evidence of a knowledge of the plants and animals living in that environment. Ask the children to read out their diary entries.

p43 Who lives there? — FINDING OUT

Learning objective
● To know that the climate affects where plants and animals live.

Lesson context
See 'Voyage of discovery' above.

Setting the homework
This activity provides an opportunity to look more widely at the four environments explored in the previous two activities. Encourage the children to use a range of information sources, including libraries and the Internet. You may need to provide books for the children to borrow.

Back at school
Encourage the children to share their findings. Discuss ways in which some of the animals are adapted to live in their particular environment – for example, a polar bear has thick white fur; a cactus has juicy flesh to store water.

p44 Habitats — SCIENCE PRACTICE

Learning objective
● To know that living things in a habitat are affected by light and shade, dryness and moisture, heat and cold.

Lesson context
Ask the children where particular minibeasts might live. What conditions are they best suited to? Take the children out to study two contrasting areas of the school grounds (such as the playground and under a hedge), recording the living things found there and the conditions. Later, ask the children to compare these environments and find out more about the plants and animals they found.

Setting the homework
This activity revises and extends the class work. Remind the children to consider all relevant conditions. Some of the choices may not be appropriate and can be ignored.

Back at school
Check that the children have completed the activity and discuss their answers. If anyone has different answers, encourage all the children to consider why that answer was given. **Answers:** woodlouse – dark, damp, cold; cactus plant – light, dry, hot; moss – light, damp; earthworm – dark, damp; snail – light, damp; sunflower – light, hot.

p45 How much waste? — NUMERACY LINK

Learning objective
● To know that there are many waste products that can affect the environment.

Lesson context
Collect and display a bag of classroom waste from one day. Discuss waste disposal, landfill sites, incinerators and recycling. Arrange a trip around the local community to identify the waste being produced by homes, transport and industry. Ask the children to draw maps of different types of waste and create posters (using pictures or samples of waste) to show the effects on the environment.

Setting the homework
Discuss the health and safety aspects of handling waste materials: making sure that the waste is clean and safe, washing hands after handling it. Remind the children to use standard measures (g and kg).

Back at school
Check that the children have used standard measures and that their figures look sensible. Discuss their findings in relation to the environment. Calculate how much of each type of waste could be recycled by the class in one week.

p46 Don't waste it, recycle it! — SCIENCE PRACTICE

Learning objective
● To know that there are many waste products that can affect the environment.

Lesson context
Talk in more detail about waste recycling. What types of waste can be recycled? Discuss any recycling the children do, and the effects on the environment of not recycling (using up natural resources, filling in of land with waste).

Setting the homework
Ask the children to imagine they are taking part in a campaign to increase the amount of waste that is recycled.

They should design an attractive poster with a clear message that will persuade people to take part.

Back at school
Look at the poster designs. Ask some children to explain the content, layout and message of their poster. Let the children swap and improve their ideas to develop a full-colour final product.

UNIT 4 MATERIALS — NATURAL & MANUFACTURED MATERIALS

p47 Inside my house — SCIENCE PRACTICE

Learning objective
● To know a range of common materials and that some materials may have different uses.

Lesson context
Ask the children to identify a range of materials, using all their senses. Ask them to find objects around the school that contain particular materials, and to say how they used their senses to identify the materials.

Setting the homework
This activity could be used at the start of a topic to assess the children's knowledge. Encourage them to use their senses and fill in the table carefully. Explain that sometimes unexpected materials are used to make a house and its contents, for example plastic doors.

Back at school
Encourage the children to share their findings. Compile a chart to show the numbers of people with, for example, window frames that are wooden, PVC and metal. Ask the children to explain why certain materials are used (for example, glass in windows).

p48 Now and then — ASK AN ADULT

Learning objective
● To know a range of common materials and that a material may have different uses.

Lesson context
Display an old object that the children may not recognise, such as a 78rpm record, flat iron or chamber pot. Discuss its uses and the materials it was made from. Ask 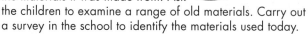 the children to examine a range of old materials. Carry out a survey in the school to identify the materials used today.

Setting the homework
Remind the children of the unusual object and its modern-day equivalents. Talk about making comparisons between new and old materials.

Back at school
Check that the children have made simple comparisons. Ask them to share their answers. **Answers:** milk container – old glass, new plastic; kettle – old metal, new plastic; clothes dryer – old wood, new metal and plastic; door – old wood, new PVC (plastic); bed warmer – old metal, new rubber or plastic. Plastic has replaced many older materials.

p49 Material adjectives — LITERACY LINK

Learning objective
● To know that any material may have more than one property.

Lesson context
Provide a selection of materials for the children to look at and handle. Encourage the children to describe them using appropriate vocabulary. Talk about how a material has several properties and different materials can share the same property. List the properties of some familiar materials.

Setting the homework
Talk about some properties the children have identified, and how we can use them to describe objects and materials in more detail. Remind the children what adjectives are. Encourage them to suggest adjectives they could use to describe, for example, paper: *crinkly, crisp, white, thin.*

Back at school
List the 'Top Ten' adjectives for each material. Check that the children have completed the task correctly and chosen suitable adjectives. These could be used for further literacy work on describing.

p50 Natural or manufactured? — FINDING OUT

Learning objective
● To know that some materials occur naturally and others do not.

Lesson context
Display a collection of objects made from familiar materials. Talk about each material's properties and uses. Encourage the children to think about its origins. Ask them to think of materials that are natural (but perhaps processed) and ones that are manufactured. Carry out a survey of manufactured and natural materials in the classroom and their uses.

Setting the homework
Remind the children that some materials occur naturally, but others are manufactured. Talk about ways of finding out about these materials, using books or the Internet. You may need to provide resources from which the children can choose items to borrow.

Back at school
Encourage the children to share their findings. Check that they have sorted the materials correctly. **Answers:** natural or processed – wool, wood, cotton, stone; manufactured – plastic, paper, polystyrene, glass. (Paper could perhaps be classified as a processed natural material.)

p51 Rocks — NUMERACY LINK

Learning objective
● To be able to recognise and describe a range of different rocks.

Lesson context
Provide a collection of rock samples for the children to look at and handle. Ask them to describe the rocks using characteristics such as colour, shape and size. Make a display of rocks with their correct names and descriptions. Ask the children to group more rocks according to their characteristics, and to draw sketches.

Setting the homework
Remind the children about the different types of rock they have looked at. Explain the activity, reminding them to be safe: to take care with heavy masses, use rounded stones rather than jagged rocks, and wash their hands and scales afterwards. Talk about estimation; reinforce the idea that

the estimated and actual masses are not exactly the same.

Back at school
Check that the children's results look sensible and that the estimated and actual masses are not identical.

p52 Soil — SCIENCE TO SHARE

Learning objective
● To know there are different kinds of soil.

Lesson context
Take into the classroom a piece of rock, some crushed rock, a container of soil, a container of water and a dead weed. Ask the children how these things are linked. Discuss the idea of soil formation. Ask the children to explain how soil is formed, using a series of annotated drawings. Examine soil samples from different locations.

Setting the homework
Explain the activity. Remind the children that to draw from observation, they need to look carefully at the size and shape of the soil particles. Ask them whether there is anything else they could include in their sketch, such as stones or minibeasts in their soil sample.

Back at school
Use the sketches as a basis for further artwork – perhaps drawings using different media, such as charcoal or pencils of varying softness.

UNIT 5 ELECTRICITY — ELECTRICITY AND COMMUNICATION

p53 There's a fault here! — SCIENCE TO SHARE

Learning objective
● To know that electricity can be dangerous and must be treated with great care.

Lesson context
As a class, list electrical appliances found in the home. Brainstorm ideas about the nature of electricity. Display some small electrical appliances. Lead the children to consider the dangers of mains electricity. Work together to write an 'Electrical Safety Code', then develop an electrical safety campaign using posters, leaflets and drama.

Setting the homework
Remind the children of their 'Electrical Safety Code'. Talk a little about how we often think accidents will never happen to us. Discuss the activity briefly.

Back at school
Talk about the dangers shown in the picture. Ask the children to share their safety slogans. Check whether they have identified the ten dangers. **Answers:** first picture – child playing with kite near overhead power lines, child climbing electricity pylon, child climbing into electricity substation, child poking at electric fence with stick; second picture – overloaded socket, teenager plugging in hair dryer while long hair is dripping over hands, adult washing up close to plugged-in radio, child poking knife into plugged-in toaster.

p54 Writing instructions LITERACY LINK

Learning objective
● To know how to make a simple circuit with a switch.

Lesson context
Provide some electrical components such as batteries and holders, bulbs, switches, buzzers, wires and crocodile clips. Ask the children to identify these. Can they make a bulb light up? Talk about the need for a complete circuit. Encourage the children to use a switch to control a circuit, to record their work in words and pictures, and to think about the different types of switches used at home and in school.

Setting the homework
Ask the children to recall how they made their circuits. Remind them about writing instructions: they should assume nothing and not leave out any steps.

Back at school
Check that the children's instructions are accurate and clear, with no steps missed out. Ask a few children to read out their instructions while someone tries to follow them exactly.

p55 Broken circuits SCIENCE PRACTICE

Learning objective
● To identify circuits that will not let electricity flow.

Lesson context
Before the lesson, prepare a number of simple circuits: some complete, others not. Start the lesson by talking about what is needed to make a circuit. Model this by standing the children in a circle, each holding a small ball: on your word, they pass the balls around the circle. Ask one child to turn sideways, not passing or receiving any balls; explain that this child is a switch. In groups, the children can then look at your circuits, predicting and testing whether the electricity will flow in each circuit.

Setting the homework
This activity revises the class work, encouraging the children to identify broken and complete circuits.

Back at school
Check the children's work, looking for the ability to identify broken circuits. Use components to demonstrate each circuit. **Answers:** 1. cross, 2. tick, 3. cross, 4. cross.

p56 Morse code SCIENCE TO SHARE

Learning objective
● To know that electricity is used for communicating with sound (light).

Lesson context
Discuss the many different ways there are of communicating. Play 'Chinese Whispers' to demonstrate that communication needs to be a two-way process. Introduce the Morse code system. Clap out some simple Morse code messages together. Talk about sending Morse code messages using sound or light. Give the children opportunities to communicate in Morse code using light and sound devices.

Setting the homework
Remind the children about Morse code. Talk about the need for accuracy. Explain the activity to the children. A second copy of the code would be helpful.

Back at school
Provide a torch. Ask the children to flash their messages while others try to decipher them. Reinforce the importance of communication.

p57 Communication survey FINDING OUT

Learning objective
● To know that electricity is used for communication systems.

Lesson context
Talk about how we can communicate using electricity. Look at examples shown in magazines. Ask the children to stick or draw pictures of computers, TV sets, radios, telephones, etc on large sheets of paper, with captions about how we use them to communicate. Groups of children can write and send a simple e-mail message, perhaps to a partner school abroad.

Setting the homework
This activity could be done before the lesson, so that the results can be used as a focus for discussion. Talk about how we can identify communication devices that use electricity: they are mains- or battery-powered.

Back at school
Use the results to show how many ways we have of communicating, and to provide data for a class graph.

p58 What's on the TV? NUMERACY LINK

Learning objective
● To know that electricity is used for communication systems.

Lesson context
See above.

Setting the homework
This activity could be given out after the lesson. Talk with the children about one of their favourite communication systems: television. Discuss how time measures are used in TV schedules and listings.

Back at school
Check that the children have answered correctly and developed their ability to use vocabulary of time.

UNIT 6 FORCES & MOTION   MAGNETS AND SPRINGS

p59 Push or pull? SCIENCE PRACTICE

Learning objective
● To know there are forces between magnets which push and pull.

Lesson context
Introduce the idea that magnets have two poles, north (N) and south (S). Let the children investigate what happens when two magnets are brought together with different combinations of the poles. Discuss their findings. Introduce vocabulary such as *repulsion*, *repel*, *attraction* and *attract*.

Setting the homework
Remind the children of their investigation, using the

appropriate vocabulary. If they have magnets at home, or they can borrow school magnets, they could carry out the homework activity practically.

Back at school
Discuss the children's findings before agreeing on a simple rule about attraction and repulsion. Mark the children's work for understanding of these concepts.

p60 The Great Magnet Game SCIENCE PRACTICE

Learning objective
● To know that some materials are magnetic and others are not.

Lesson context
Which materials do the children think will be attracted by magnets? Compile a list before carrying out a practical activity to test various materials and objects. Discuss the results, then ask the children to carry out a survey of metal objects around the school (including some copper or aluminium items). Are they all magnetic?

Setting the homework
This activity builds on the class work. Remind the children that not all metals are attracted by magnets.

Back at school
Discuss the activity. Compile a list of materials attracted and not attracted by magnets. Encourage the children to draw some conclusions from these lists.

p61 Jack in the Box SCIENCE TO SHARE

Learning objective
● To know that springs and elastic bands exert forces.

Lesson context
Talk about forces, developing the idea that forces are pushes or pulls. Let the children handle springs. Introduce the concept of 'opposite' forces: you push on the spring and it pushes back on you. Let the children explore the forces exerted by springs and elastic bands, describing what they experience.

Setting the homework
This activity develops a practical use for the concept of a spring exerting a force. Discuss the importance of cutting out the net carefully. Demonstrate how to make the box, and how to make the paper 'spring'. This activity will be much easier if the page is copied onto thin card (and preferably enlarged to A3).

Back at school
Ask the children to demonstrate their Jack in the Box models. Make a display of these.

p62 Stretchy elastic SCIENCE TO SHARE

Learning objective
● To know that the force exerted by an elastic band depends on how much it is stretched.

Lesson context
Under safe conditions, test a few toy catapults to see which will project an object the furthest. Discuss fair testing and whether it is fair if different children test the catapults. Use a flat board catapult (see illustration below) to investigate how the pull on the elastic affects the distance a toy car travels. The children could make simple elastic-driven paddle boats.

Setting the homework
Discuss the task, having prepared a similar force meter. You may need to provide paper fasteners, paper clips and elastic bands, perhaps in small plastic money bags. Remind the children to measure carefully. Discuss what measures are suitable, and how to read a scale to the nearest division. Remind them not to weigh heavy items.

Back at school
Ask some children to demonstrate their force meters. Reinforce the idea that the elastic stretches further when a greater force is applied to it.

p63 Vehicle building LITERACY LINK

Learning objective
● To know that energy can change forms.

Lesson context
Where do the children think energy comes from? Explain that energy cannot be created or destroyed, only changed so that we experience it differently. Identify the energy change in a CD player (electrical to sound). Discuss stored energy and movement energy, using elastic bands and springs. Let the children design and build model vehicles that use the stored energy of an elastic band.

Setting the homework
This activity follows on from the lesson and consolidates literacy skills. Talk with the class about the steps they went through in building their models. Encourage them to write the steps in the correct, logical order. Communicating their design ideas is an important design and technology skill to reinforce here.

Back at school
Mark the children's work, looking for a clear and logical sequence of instructions. These could be displayed alongside the model vehicles.

p64 Energy and fuel FINDING OUT

Learning objectives
● To know that heat is a form of energy and it may be supplied by several sources.
● To know that energy can change forms.

Lesson context
Revise the idea of energy transfer before discussing heat as energy. Talk about how we use heat and the fuels that provide it. Ask the children to consider how they use energy in moving, and to record whether they feel warmer after exercise.

Setting the homework
Remind the children about energy transfer and fuels as energy sources. You may need to provide reference books to help them find out how one type of fossil fuel was formed. Make sure that they are covering the three types of fossil fuel between them. They could use www.energy.ca.gov/education to search for information.

Back at school
Mark the children's work to see whether they have identified energy transfers correctly. Encourage them to share their findings about fuels. Compile these into a class fact sheet.

UNIT 7 LIGHT & SOUND — SOURCES AND EFFECTS

p65 Me and my shadow — LITERACY LINK

Learning objective
● To know that when light from the Sun is blocked by an object, a shadow forms.

Lesson context
Encourage the children to share ideas about the formation of shadows. Use an OHP to demonstrate how shadows are formed. Discuss the Sun as our major source of natural light. Outside, carry out an activity in which the children observe and draw their shadows at various times of the day. Emphasise the importance of not looking directly at the Sun.

Setting the homework
This activity encourages children to describe and sequence key incidents. Revise how shadows are formed. Discuss adjectives that could be used to describe shadows, and explain that a storyboard shows the main incidents in a story. Explain that while the events are fictional, they should use their scientific knowledge to make sure the light and shadows are realistic.

Back at school
Compare the children's storyboards. Look for evidence of a sequence of events. Later, use the storyboards as a basis for further creative writing.

p66 Light sources — SCIENCE PRACTICE

Learning objective
● To know that when light from sources other than the Sun is blocked, shadows are also produced.

Lesson context
Compile a list of light sources other than the Sun. Discuss their importance for us. Use a variety of light sources to cast shadows, asking the children to observe and consider the effect of moving the light source nearer to the object. Carry out a survey of light sources around the school.

Setting the homework
Briefly revise how shadows are formed. How do we cope with the darkness at night? Remind the children of the light sources they identified.

Back at school
Discuss the difference between light sources and reflectors of light. **Answers:** light sources – a star, the Sun, a fire, the TV, a candle; reflect light – clothes, the Moon, a book. The TV may cause some debate, as the screen is a light source but also reflects light.

p67 Car colour survey — NUMERACY LINK

Learning objective
● To know that colours are used for decoration and to give messages in the man-made world.

Lesson context
Discuss the importance of colour in the natural world (for example, camouflage) and the built environment (for example, road safety). Make a list of things whose colour is important. Talk about how traffic lights operate and what the colours mean. Can the children recall their sequence? Look at other uses of colour, outdoors and indoors.

Setting the homework
Discuss the importance of colour, and how people often have favourite colours. Talk about carrying out a traffic survey, and the importance of doing this from a safe place. The activity is designed to reinforce skills in data handling, so remind the children about tally marks and drawing bar charts (one block represents one car).

Back at school
Collate the children's results to find the top five colours for cars.

p68 Musical instruments — FINDING OUT

Learning objective
● To know that there is a wide variety of sound sources.

Lesson context
Ask the children to close their eyes and listen to the sounds around them. Compile a class list of sounds and group them according to source: natural, human, machines. Ask the children to carry out a sound survey around the school, recording the sounds heard in different places on a plan of the school building, and then write a report identifying the noisy and quiet areas.

Setting the homework
Ask the children to recall the sounds they heard. Were they natural or man-made, pleasant or unpleasant? Say that music can be any of these. Talk through the activity.

Back at school
Ask the children to share their findings and explain how sounds are produced with each instrument. Compile a list of woodwind, percussion, brass, stringed and keyboard instruments.

p68 Making music — SCIENCE PRACTICE

Learning objective
● To know that of the many sounds around us at any one time some are loud, some are soft/quiet, some are high- and others are low-pitched.

Lesson context
Let the children play some unpitched percussion instruments. Talk about the sounds produced when they are hit gently or hard. Introduce the concepts of volume and pitch, using a piano: the pitch depends on the length of the string, the volume on how hard the key is struck. Carry out a survey as in 'Musical instruments', asking the children to record the pitch and volume of sounds using their own colour-coding system.

Setting the homework
Reinforce the idea that by using musical instruments, we can vary the pitch and volume of sounds. Discuss the task, reminding the children to keep their instrument simple. Show them examples such as yoghurt-pot shakers or elastic-band harps.

Back at school
Ask the children to demonstrate their instruments. Later, they could work in groups to compose and perform a piece of music.

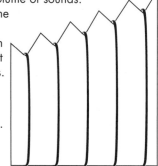

p70 Sound words — LITERACY LINK

Learning objective
● To know about some of the uses of sound.

Lesson context
Ask the children to use secondary sources of information to find out as much as they can about how sounds are used – for example, to communicate, to entertain or to warn. They should consider natural as well as man-made sounds – for example, how birds communicate using sounds.

Setting the homework
Discuss how certain animals and objects make particular sounds. Ask the children to think of the words that we use to describe these sounds. Talk about acrostic poems, reminding the children that their poem does not need to rhyme. This activity will further develop the children's vocabulary.

Back at school
Check the children's answers and encourage them to share their poems. **Answers:** 1. roar, 2. slam, 3. bleat, 4. creak, 5. neigh, 6. patter, 7. meow, 8. beat, 9. growl, 10. clatter.

UNIT 8 EARTH & BEYOND — THE SUN AND SHADOWS

p71 Shadow puppets — SCIENCE TO SHARE

Learning objective
● To know that shadows are formed when objects block light from the Sun.

Lesson context
Give the children a riddle about a mystery object: a shadow. When they have solved it, discuss how shadows are formed and use an OHP or torch to demonstrate. Talk about how shadows cast by the Sun move during the day. Ask the children to match some shadows to the objects that cast them, and to tell you how shadows are formed.

Setting the homework
This activity extends the class work. Remind the children how shadows are created. Ask them to think about the size of the shadows they are making.

Back at school
Ask the children to display their shadow puppets and explain what they have found out. Check that their drawings show a larger shadow when the puppet is closer to the light source.

p72 Shadow lengths — NUMERACY LINK

Learning objectives
● To know that the shape and position of a shadow change at different times of day.
● To be able to measure in standard measures and present results in tables and bar charts.

Lesson context
Set up some posts outside. At regular intervals through the day, measure and record the shadow lengths together. Tabulate the results and draw a bar chart for each post.

Setting the homework
This activity could usefully be set before the main lesson. Remind the children to measure and record carefully. If necessary, make sure that they understand how to present

their results as a bar chart. Most children should use a 1:1 scale, but some may be able to use 1:2.

Back at school
Check that the children's bar charts are accurate and match the data collected. Can they explain why the shadow can be longer or shorter than the object? Discuss why the shadows are shorter at midday and longer near sunset.

p73 The Sun in the sky — SCIENCE PRACTICE

Learning objective
● To know that the Sun appears to follow a curved path across the sky every day.

Lesson context
Early in the day, take the children outside to draw a landscape scene. Throughout the day, mark the position of the Sun (and the time) on the drawing to plot its apparent movement. Set up a small 'sunshine recorder' using a dowel in a pot (see below). Mark the end of the shadow with a cross. Join up the marks to show a curved path.

Setting the homework
Remind the children of the class activity. Encourage them to carry out individual observations. Stress the importance of not looking directly at the Sun.

Back at school
Check that the children's drawings show the Sun travelling in an arc across the sky. Relate their shadow observations to the changing position of the Sun: the shadows are shorter when the Sun is 'higher' in the sky.

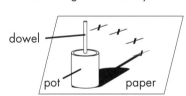

p74 The Sun — FINDING OUT

Learning objective
● To understand that the Sun is at the centre of the Solar System and the Earth orbits it.

Lesson context
Talk about how the Sun is at the centre of our Solar System with the planets orbiting around it. Use children to model the Earth rotating on its axis as it orbits the Sun. Use a globe and an OHP or torch to model the effect of this on the day and night. Ask the children to use secondary sources to find out more about the Sun.

Setting the homework
Suggest that the children use the questions on the sheet as a starter to get them thinking. Encourage them not just to copy large sections of text, but to read the information and note key phrases they can use in their own sentences.

Back at school
Let the children present their findings to each other, perhaps within a time limit (such as a minute per child).

p75 The Solar System — LITERACY LINK

Learning objective
● To understand that the Sun is at the centre of the Solar System and the Earth orbits it.

Lesson context
Use the children to model the Solar System: nine planets orbiting the Sun. Give them an exercise: matching pairs of phrases to make sentences about the Solar System. Ask them to use secondary sources to compile planet factfiles or a 'Solar System Quiz'.

Setting the homework
Explain that people once believed the Earth was at the centre of the Solar System. Ask the children to become newspaper reporters. Encourage them not to just copy sections of text from a source, but to read and rewrite. Note-taking and rewriting in a different style are important literacy skills for Year 3 in the NLS for England.

Back at school
Read the children's work for accuracy. Ask some children to present their writing as a TV or radio news bulletin.

p76 Sundials — FINDING OUT

Learning objective
● To know that shadows can be used to tell the approximate time of day.

Lesson context
Ask the children how they know the time. Talk about sand timers and water clocks. Introduce the idea of a sundial. Set up a model sundial. Can the children use it to tell the time? Ask them to make simple stick sundials and calibrate them at hourly intervals.

Setting the homework
Demonstrate how to make the sundial. Talk about designs for the sundial faces: these could be pictures (such as a place) or patterns. Explain how to calibrate the dial using the sun and a watch or clock.

Back at school
Encourage the children to share their designs and results.

UNIT 1 OURSELVES — HOW I MOVE

p77 X-ray observation — SCIENCE PRACTICE

Learning objectives
● To know that the skeleton is made from bones.
● To understand that we have lots of joined bones to give a greater range of movement.
● To make observations.

Lesson context
The children work in groups, looking at how dolls move and comparing this to how we move. Discuss their observations, using a model skeleton to show how the bones and joints enable us to move. Label the spine, skull and ribs and ask them to find those parts on themselves and label them on a drawing, then explore the movement of different joints.

Setting the homework
Ask the children to observe the bones and movements of their hands in detail, and to record what they observe.

Back at school
Try the hand movement activity together, comparing the class results with the homework observations. Praise particularly detailed efforts. Use the class skeleton to demonstrate model answers.

p78 Growing Gallery — SCIENCE TO SHARE

Learning objectives
● To know that a skeleton grows from birth to adulthood.
● To consider what sources of information they will use to answer questions.

Lesson context
Compare pictures of different-aged people, relating the differences to the skeleton. Look at the forearm and discuss how it has developed since birth and will continue to develop. Groups measure and compare forearms.

Setting the homework
This activity will help the children to personalise observations made in the lesson. Stress the importance of comparing their bone lengths to those of their helper.

Back at school
Compare the findings. Ask questions such as: *Who was the biggest baby? Who had the smallest feet when they started school?* Make a class 'Growing Gallery' or a pictogram.

p79 Dr Dreadful's disaster — SCIENCE PRACTICE

Learning objectives
● To know that the skeleton supports and protects organs in the body.
● To locate and name some organs of the body.

Lesson context
Discuss what is inside our bodies. Draw a body outline and ask the children to suggest the major organs, what they do and where they are. Groups research these ideas, using books and CD-ROMs. Draw a simple class version of 'Our Insides'.

Setting the homework
This activity connects class work on the skeleton and body organs. Enlarging the sheet to A3 size will be helpful.

Back at school
Discuss the answers. Show the children how to feel their heartbeat. Try counting the ribs. **Answers:** The skull protects the brain; the rib cage protects the heart and lungs.

p80 Top of the hops — NUMERACY LINK

Learning objectives
● To know that the action of muscles helps the body to move.
● To observe their own bodies closely.

Lesson context
Use the homework as preparation for the lesson. Make a model of the elbow joint, using rulers and elastic to demonstrate the paired muscles. The children make models, relating them to their own movements.

Setting the homework
This activity links to the NNS objective of using graphs to solve problems. Discuss the movements we make, and the body parts we use for different tasks. Encourage more able children to use a scale of 1:2 on the vertical axis.

Back at school
Ask groups to show their findings and others to check their answers. Look at how muscles enable us to move.
Answers: The arms and hands were probably used most, the jaw least; they could increase the amount the jaw is used (not usually a problem in most classes!) by talking, chewing gum or drinking.

p81 Workout NUMERACY LINK

Learning objectives
- To know that when muscles work hard in exercise they also affect the body in other ways.
- To relate their work in science to PE.

Lesson context
Before a PE lesson discuss what the children use to play sports (muscles and bones). Set activities that use different muscles, focusing on the thigh and bicep muscles. Ask the children to compare how they feel before, during and after exercise.

Setting the homework
This activity involves making and recording measurements. Model accurate measuring as a reminder. Demonstrate how to 'measure around' if the children are unsure.

Back at school
Discuss the workout. Compare how different children felt after the exercises. Use the data to draw a class graph. Link the results to previous class discussions about how limbs move through the action of paired muscles on bones.
Answers: Measurements should be greater for tensed than relaxed muscles.

p82 Frazzle a friend! FINDING OUT

Learning objectives
- To use secondary sources of information to answer questions.
- To assess the children's knowledge and understanding of the skeletal system.

Lesson context
This activity gives the children an opportunity to use research skills towards the end of this unit, prior to assessment.

Setting the homework
List examples of research sources the children use: football league tables, TV listings and so on. Make a list of further sources together. Stress that the quiz format allows them to use any sources they find as much as they like.

Back at school
Discuss the sources the children used. Ask them which were most useful, and discuss common difficulties.
Answers: 206 bones; move; back; any vertebrates. Use the 'Frazzle a friend' section for a class quiz.

UNIT 2 ANIMALS & PLANTS | DIFFERENT SORTS OF SKELETONS

p83 Sort and Snap SCIENCE TO SHARE

Learning objective
- To understand that a wide range of living things can be classified as plants or as animals.

Lesson context
Provide a collection of labelled pictures of living things. The children work in groups to find different ways of sorting them: size, colour and so on. They should record their criteria and results. As a class, sort all the pictures into *Plants* and *Animals*.

Setting the homework
Stress that the children can use any sources of information. Make a list of sources. Remind them of the rules of 'Snap'.

Enlarging the homework sheet to A3 size and copying it onto card will be helpful.

Back at school
Let the children share and compare their cards. Show different examples and make sure there are no cars or buildings. Highlight any unusual suggestions. Combine three or four sets of cards for a class game.

p84 Midnight at the House of Doom! LITERACY LINK

Learning objective
- To know that bones have features that can be compared.

Lesson context
Use a 'feely bag' to introduce a collection of sterilised bones (from various animals). A skull makes a dramatic start! Look at some bone samples and encourage questions and comparisons. The children work in pairs to share words or phrases as a basis for descriptive writing about bones.

Setting the homework
Introduce the idea of a party filled with different kinds of skeletons. *What might you see?* Make a class list of ideas, and use the brainstormed words from the lesson as a starting point for individual poems.

Back at school
Share the children's writing and encourage them to use their jaws to read their poems to the class. Use all the writing in a display or an assembly.

p85 Inside story SCIENCE PRACTICE

Learning objective
- To recognise similarities and differences between different groups of vertebrates.

Lesson context
This homework will elicit your class's ideas about different kinds of skeletons. It can serve as preparation for a lesson in which you introduce the classification of animals according to whether they have a backbone.

Setting the homework
Stress that the children should look at the shapes of animals and the ways in which they move in order to build up a mental picture of their skeleton. Relate this to previous classwork on the human skeleton. Reassure them that there are no 'wrong' answers, as they are making a prediction.

Back at school
Compare predictions and encourage children to share their reasoning. Reveal the factual answers using pictures.
Answers: Goldfish and giraffes are vertebrates; tarantulas are not. Amazingly, giraffes have the same number of neck bones as humans!

p86 Take care! FINDING OUT

Learning objective
- To know how to collect animals sensitively.

Lesson context
Contrast creatures that have different skeletons. Collect some invertebrates with the children. Worms, slugs and snails have water skeletons; spiders and millipedes have outside skeletons. Ask the children to use magnifying glasses to examine and draw the creatures. Stress that they

need care when collected and must be returned to their habitats as quickly as possible.

Setting the homework
This activity focuses on why we should respect any creatures we collect. Talk about pets at home. Stress how we feel when we are respected. Show some examples of information leaflets (on other issues).

Back at school
In groups, the children can look at the finished leaflets. Ask one child from each group to explain what they have produced. Praise well-researched or well-presented efforts. The leaflets could be developed as an ICT project.
Answers: The leaflet should address breathing, feeding and drinking; some children may also have considered habitats.

p87 Guests at the House of Doom
SCIENCE PRACTICE

Learning objective
● To know how a decision tree can be used to classify.

Lesson context
Introduce the concept of a yes/no decision tree by using one to sort a collection of familiar animals into vertebrates and invertebrates. The children work in groups to identifying further examples, using the same decision tree.

Setting the homework
This activity reinforces the skills introduced in the lesson. Stress that although the subject matter is different, the principle is the same and some of the questions are similar. Run through an example together.

Back at school
Go through the decision tree process together. Invent and use one that applies to a school situation.
Answers: 1. Rockard, 2. Sneak, 3. Lady Cobweb, 4. Blur, 5. Splat, 6. Professor Fang, 7. Narkella, 8. Skelly Tony. Lord Withers saw Rockard.

p88 Sort it out!
NUMERACY LINK

Learning objective
● To assess the children's knowledge of the kinds of skeletons and of the way animals are classified.

Lesson context
Give the children pictures of a range of animals. Ask them to observe the shapes and sizes of the animals and group them according to similarities (using their recent class work to help them), then stick down and label the pictures according to how they have sorted them.

Setting the homework
This activity requires data handling skills. Stress that the children are approaching it with knowledge, and that the 'Bonus Boxes' are an opportunity to research further. Enlarging the homework sheet to A3 size will be helpful.

Back at school
Compare the children's graphs. Ask volunteers to present their graphs to the class, explaining where their 'Bonus Box' choices fitted and why. **Answers:** bone skeleton – human, fish, tiger, snake; water skeleton – slug; outside skeleton – spider.

UNIT 3 THE ENVIRONMENT
HABITATS AND FOOD CHAINS

p89 My scrapbook
LITERACY LINK

Learning objectives
● To elicit children's ideas about living things.
● To know that there is a wide variety of organisms on the planet.

Lesson context
The children sort pictures of living and non-living things (only use the term *dead* for things that were once alive); record the results using sketches, words or a graph; and explain their decisions and list common features in each category.

Setting the homework
This activity links to the NLS for Year 4, which requires children to collect information from a variety of sources and present it in one simple format. Explain the idea of a scrapbook, and use familiar examples of an introduction and a contents page as reminders. This activity can be set for two weeks to half a term. You could provide A4 sugar paper scrapbooks (two A3 sheets folded and stapled).

Back at school
Compare findings. Let some children read from their introductions. Encourage the children to swap scrapbooks at reading time. Display the books in the class library.
Answers: picture 3.

p90 Miss Harvey's habitat
NUMERACY LINK

Learning objectives
● To investigate the plants found in a certain habitat.
● To compare the numbers of different types of plant in two habitats.
● To suggest reasons for differences in the plants that grow in different habitats.
● To devise their own record sheet.

Lesson context
Discuss the differences between two habitats, such as *Under the tree* and *In the playground*. Can the children predict what plants live in each habitat? How could they record their findings? Recording grass is a good opportunity to estimate! After your field trip, compare the plants and contrast their habitats, asking the children to explain their findings.

Setting the homework
Recap the estimation skills used in the lesson, focusing on rounding. These skills are objectives of the NNS. Remind the children how to draw graph axes.

Back in school
Ask the children to estimate how many of them are in class today, then count accurately and round the number to the nearest ten. Mark the homework as a class. Use the graphs for a display. **Answers:** 17cm; 20cm; 12cm; 10cm; 76cm; 80cm.

p91 Ideal Homes Exhibition
SCIENCE PRACTICE

Learning objectives
● To communicate findings about the habitats investigated.

● To begin to explore the relationships between the physical aspects and the plants and animals living in a habitat.

Lesson context
Following a class investigation into local habitats, ask questions such as: *Why did we find woodlice under the stones but not in the playing field?* Compile a habitat checklist that includes shelter, food, safety from predators and growing conditions. The children work collaboratively on a class book about habitats.

Setting the homework
Enlarge the homework sheet to A3 size. Talk about where humans commonly live and why. Refer to your checklist to make links with other organisms.

Back at school
Compare answers and discuss how the children made their decisions. **Answers:** fungi – rotting log; shark – sea; woodlouse – under a stone; worm – soil; reed – pond; blackbird – tree. The children's choice of habitats should relate to the criteria in your class checklist.

p92 What's for dinner? SCIENCE PRACTICE

Learning objectives
● To understand what is meant by a food chain.
● To know what the words *producer* and *consumer* mean.

Lesson context
List foods the children like to eat. Talk about why we need to eat (to gain energy, grow and stay alive). Draw a food chain with arrows: wheat to chickens to humans. Explain that this food chain involves a producer (wheat) and two consumers (chickens, humans). Ask groups to construct food chains for the other foods in the class list.

Setting the homework
The activity applies this knowledge to a meal eaten at home. Encourage the children to think of themselves as *consumers* at the end of a food chain.

Back at school
Go through the answers. Compare the children's meals and the food chains they were part of. **Answers:** plant (producer), fly (consumer), vole (consumer), fox (consumer); grass (producer), cow (consumer), Professor Fumble (consumer).

p93 What's cooking? SCIENCE TO SHARE

Learning objectives
● To understand the terms *herbivore* and *carnivore*.
● To understand that food chains are part of more complex food webs.

Lesson context
Discuss animals eaten by more than one predator (slugs are eaten by birds, foxes and hedgehogs). Explain the term *food web*. Provide pictures of animals and plants; ask groups to draw arrows between them to show feeding relationships. Use the terms *carnivore* and *herbivore*.

Setting the homework
Remind the children of the vocabulary from the lesson. Discuss traditional foods that we eat at certain times, and other reasons why we eat particular foods.

Back at school
Ask groups to compare their answers and lists, coming together to compare favourite foods and their sources. List

the children's questions and use them for discussion or research. **Answers:** meat – sausage, bacon, black pudding; vegetables – chips, mushrooms; the egg is neither (it is a dairy product).

p94 Dinner for two? SCIENCE PRACTICE

Learning objectives
● To understand the terms *herbivore* and *carnivore*.
● To understand that food chains are part of more complex food webs.

Lesson context
This activity develops the content of the previous activity. It can be used at any point towards the end of the unit.

Setting the homework
Discuss favourite foods. Introduce the words *omnivore* and *vegetarian*. Explain that humans are natural omnivores, but some choose to be vegetarians. Are any of the children vegetarian? If so, what does this mean to them?

Back at school
Draw or list the foods from the sheet on a board or flip chart. Ask for volunteers to play the roles of the people and zoo animals. Allow the children to mark each other's homework as they go along. **Answers:** The lion and crocodile (carnivores) will eat steak and chicken; the antelope (herbivore) will eat beans, grass and leaves; the chimpanzee (omnivore) will eat all of these. Sam would eat tomato soup, cheesy baked potato, broccoli and stilton quiche and toffee ice cream; Rosa would eat all the foods. Four items have a line and a circle.

p95 Disappearing aliens SCIENCE PRACTICE

Learning objective
● To know that camouflage helps some animals to survive.

Lesson context
Read 'How the Leopard Got His Spots' by Rudyard Kipling. Discuss how and why the animals changed their skins. Use the word *camouflage* and ask for other examples. Talk about examples from nature, such as green grasshoppers and snails with stripy shells. The children paint different habitats for animal cut-outs and decide which give the best camouflage.

Setting the homework
Enlarge the homework sheet to A3 size. Stress the importance of following the colour key with the first picture. Reinforce the meaning of *camouflage*.

Back at school
Groups present their artwork and compare its effect from different distances. Children at the back of the class may have different opinions. Discuss why this is. Praise efforts that incorporate shapes (as well as colours) like those of the two aliens. Use the pictures to start a class gallery.

p96 Park life SCIENCE PRACTICE

Learning objectives
● To know that seasonal changes influence animals and plants in a habitat.
● To know that nature changes habitats.
● To understand some of our seasonal responses in order to help wildlife.

Lesson context
Choose an outdoor location for a field trip. Discuss how it

looks in other seasons. Ask the children to look for animal and plant life, and how these are affected by the seasons. Back at school, the children each write a 'diary' for a different plant or animal through the year.

Setting the homework
Distribute copies of the homework sheet (enlarging it to A3 size will be helpful). Discuss how our behaviour (what we wear, eat and do) changes with the seasons. Stress that the seasons form a cycle. You could describe how this is different in other climates.

Back at school
Display the pictures as a class gallery. Ask the children to describe and explain the seasonal changes.

UNIT 4 MATERIALS — WARM LIQUIDS, COOL SOLIDS

p97 Material world — SCIENCE PRACTICE

Learning objectives
● To elicit children's existing understanding about materials.
● To develop observation and sorting skills.

Lesson context
Provide a collection of items (metal pan, woolly glove, plastic beaker and so on). The children take turns describing them. Reinforce the word *material* as meaning whatever something is made from. Make links between what an item is made of and what it is used for. Groups sketch and describe the items, and play '20 Questions' with them.

Setting the homework
In this activity, the children will apply observation skills to the home. You could start them off by looking at the materials used in the classroom.

Back at school
Compare the examples found by the children. List all the different things they found made of each material.

p98 Where in the world? — NUMERACY LINK

Learning objectives
● To know that a thermometer is an instrument for measuring temperature.
● To measure using standard units with an appropriate degree of accuracy.

Lesson context
Pass around a bowl of ice cubes and a covered hot water bottle. Ask the children to describe them. Explain how temperature can be measured. Show a large drawing of a thermometer. After a safety talk, show the children how to use a thermometer. Set them to measure and record the temperatures of warm and cold water.

Setting the homework
Copying the sheet at A3 size will be helpful. The activity uses thermometer reading skills and develops tens and units addition and subtraction. Adding together temperatures from the class work will demonstrate the maths.

Back at school
Go through the answers together. Let the children ask their own quiz questions. **Answers:** 29°C, 9°C, 19°C, show 42°C; 1. 71°C, 2. Jhaneal, 3. 23, 4. 10.

p99 Blake's temperature trauma — NUMERACY LINK

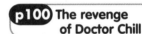

Learning objective
● To describe and suggest explanations for temperature findings.

Lesson context
Review how to use a thermometer. The children predict the temperature in different parts of the classroom: radiator, window, doorway and so on. Groups measure the temperatures, report their findings and compare them to the predictions.

Setting the homework
Enlarging the sheet to A3 size will be helpful. This activity links to the skill of solving a problem by interpreting data from a graph. Talk about weather reports and weather forecasts. How are forecasts presented? Review bar graph reading and drawing skills.

Back at school
Ask the children to compare their answers and fill in an enlarged class copy of the sheet. Ask volunteers to read and present their weather reports and compare the different data sources. **Answers:** 21°C; 28°C; Wednesday; 15°C; 20.

p100 The revenge of Doctor Chill — LITERACY LINK

Learning objective
● To know that the heat insulation properties of materials can be compared by investigation.

Lesson context
Hand around some ice pops. Use the word *melting* before investigating how different materials (including newspapers and fabric) can slow down this process. The children make predictions, measure times and record them in a table.

Setting the homework
This activity links to the skill of writing an explanation, using conventions identified through reading. Read through the cartoon together and explain that the characters need to use skills from today's lesson. Encourage the children to look closely at Zap's survival kit. Enlarging the sheet to A3 size will be helpful.

Back at school
Go through the survival kit and ask why some items are useful. Use the cartoons for a class book. **Answers:** The candle and matches will be useful (the bandage could also be set on fire).

p101 At home with Zip and Zap — SCIENCE PRACTICE

Learning objectives
● To know that some materials can be classified as solids and some as liquids.
● To be able to describe some of the properties of solids and liquids.

Lesson context
The children find adjectives to describe a block of wood and water in a cup as they pass them around. Contrast these adjectives and introduce the words *solid* and *liquid*. The children classify a collection of materials as solids or liquids in a Venn diagram.

Setting the homework
This activity requires the children to apply classification

skills to the home setting. Stress the need to observe closely.

Back at school
Split the class into two groups: one to list the solids and the other the liquids they found in the picture and at home. Make a class list. **Answers:** Star Cola, fishtank water and rain are liquids; all the other objects are solids.

---

p102 Jelly journal | SCIENCE TO SHARE

Learning objectives
- To know that a solid can be changed into a liquid by melting, and a liquid can be changed into a solid by freezing.
- To know that melting and freezing can be reversed, and are the reverse of each other.
- To make predictions and practise observation skills.

Lesson context
Provide chocolate, ice cubes, butter and wax. Investigate the effect of heating each with a small candle, then letting it cool down. The children record the name of each material, a prediction and what they observe.

Setting the homework
Talk through the instructions on a jelly packet. Stress that a helper is needed for safety and to share predictions.

Back at school
Compare predictions and observations. Talk through the jelly-making process. If necessary, you could repeat this activity in class. **Answers:** solid; liquid; any prediction is valid; solid; the coolness solidified the jelly.

UNIT 5 ELECTRICITY | SWITCHES AND CONDUCTION

---

p103 Light me! | SCIENCE REVISION

Learning objective
- To review work on electricity from Year 3/Primary 4, including the idea that a complete circuit is needed for a device to work.

Lesson context
Ask what your class know about how electrical devices work. Use a CD player and a Gameboy to compare mains and battery devices. Distribute drawings of different circuits, asking which ones will work and why. The children work in pairs to share ideas about electricity.

Setting the homework
Focus on how the drawings represent an electrical circuit. Model drawing a circuit, asking volunteers to label it.

Back at school
Fill in an enlarged copy of the sheet, comparing explanations. Draw incorrect circuits with more bulbs and switches, and challenge the children to make them work. **Answers:** No; circuit B; because the switch is 'on' and the circuit is completed; because the battery is not connected to the bulb *or* there is no wire from the switch to the bulb.

---

p104 Batteries or mains? | SCIENCE REVISION

Learning objective
As for 'Light me!' above.

Lesson context
As for 'Light me!' above.

Setting the homework
This activity can be used as preparation for the lesson described above or to reinforce the first part of it. Model drawing a bar chart, and remind the children of the importance of not touching plugs.

Back at school
Put the children back into their brainstorming pairs and ask them to compare their lists and charts, recording new facts in their 'My ideas about electricity' notes from the lesson.

---

p105 Delivery day | SCIENCE PRACTICE

Learning objective
- To know that mains electricity is a form of energy that has been converted from other forms of energy.

Lesson context
Ask: *Where do you think mains electricity comes from?* Record the answers. Demonstrate a toy windmill. Discuss how wind power can be used to grind corn or to drive the turbines in power stations. Visit a local power station. The children use secondary sources to explore your question.

Setting the homework
This activity focuses on what electricity is used for. Talk about computer games and household appliances that use electricity to do different jobs.

Back at school
Group the items, adding the children's examples. Discuss how they added the four digits, encouraging mental strategies. **Answers:** heat – kettle, fire, microwave; cool – fridge; light – lamp, torch; move – toothbrush, whisk, fan, washing machine; 4, 2, 3, 5, 14.

---

p106 The Insulation Station | LITERACY LINK

Learning objective
- To know that electricity flows through some materials and not others.

Lesson context
Ask the class what materials they have observed electricity travelling through. Make a list. Do they think electricity can travel through everything? The children work in groups with a collection of materials to predict which ones conduct electricity, then devise a way of testing them. Share methods and results, and compare with the predictions.

Setting the homework
This activity links to writing an explanation of a process using conventions identified through reading – a Year 4 NLS objective. Read through the cartoon together, focusing on the sequential and presentational conventions used.

Back at school
Go through the survival kit, asking the children why they used or rejected each item. Use the cartoons for a class book highlighting good use of cartoon conventions. **Answers:** Paper clips and foil are the only conductors.

---

p107 Circus circuits | SCIENCE TO SHARE

Learning objectives
- To know that batteries may be connected together to provide greater electrical power.
- To follow their own lines of enquiry.

Lesson context
Show the class a collection of batteries, asking why

---

different types are needed. Open a torch and ask which battery will fit. Ask what will happen to the brightness of a bulb if it is linked to more than one battery. Groups investigate the effects of using more than one battery or a different battery on circuits, bulbs and buzzers.

Setting the homework
Introduce the word *components* for the parts of an electrical circuit. Remind the children about the lesson when they added various materials to a circuit (see notes for page 106).

Back at school
Enlarge the sheet and ask volunteers to demonstrate their circuits. Compare the circuits and ask what other components could be used to light the poster more (such as a more powerful battery).

p108 Stand back, Zip and Zap!   LITERACY LINK

Learning objective
● To communicate ideas about electricity.

Lesson context
The children model a circuit by passing tennis balls around a circle. Model buzzers, switches and batteries. Groups each take a component such as *batteries* or *switches*, devise an improvisation and present it to the class.

Setting the homework
This activity links to a Year 4 NLS objective: the use of subheadings to order and improve the cohesion of written instructions. Praise the children's hard work and reflect on what they have learned. Can they write an information pamphlet? Focus on the list of subheadings on the sheet. Look at examples of information writing.

Back at school
Discuss the main points in the pamphlets. Use them in a presentation or display. **Answers:** Zip should plug the CD player into the mains; Zap should dry her hands, as water conducts electricity; overloading a socket can cause a fire.

UNIT 6 FORCES & MOTION	FRICTION

p109 Push, pull or twist dominoes   SCIENCE TO SHARE

Learning objectives
● To revise previous work on forces and to elicit children's current understanding.
● To know that a force acts in a particular direction and this can be represented by an arrow.

Lesson context
Write *push*, *pull* and *twist* on a board or flip chart. Encourage the children to give examples from everyday life. Provide them with a collection of magnets and paper clips to explore. Ask them to describe and draw what effect the magnet has on the paper clips, using an arrow to show any push, pull or twist.

Setting the homework
Remind the children how to play dominoes. Explain that they have to complete the sets of dominoes and use them in a game. Enlarge the activity sheet to A3 size.

Back at school
Look at the children's domino sets. Ask them to share these with the class and explain their choices. Play a bumper round with combined domino sets.

p110 Siân's speedy skittles 1   SCIENCE PRACTICE

Learning objectives
● To make predictions and test them.
● To compare results with predictions.
● To know that friction is a force.
● To know that friction depends on the surfaces in contact.

Lesson context
Explain that friction is the force between two surfaces that slows motion. Hook a newton meter around a brick. Ask the children to predict which surface will require most force to pull the brick along. Record the predictions before groups test the surfaces. Compare the results to the predictions. Classify the surfaces as *smooth* and *rough*.

Setting the homework
This activity allows the children to feel friction by making crayon rubbings. Model taking a clean rubbing.

Back at school
Compare the rubbings in groups. What is the most common answer? Ask the children why the answer was not always the same. **Answers:** The best surface gave the least friction during rubbing (probably tile).

p111 Friction Rollerball   NUMERACY LINK

Learning objectives
● To know that the force of friction depends on the surfaces in contact.
● To carry out a fair test.

Lesson context
Measure friction by using a shoe on a ramp: increase the height of the ramp until the shoe slips. Change the ramp surface and repeat the process, focusing on fair testing. Provide shoes with different grips and ask the children to make predictions, then carry out fair tests in groups. Compare results to predictions. Ask why some soles have a better grip than others.

Setting the homework
This activity links to use of mathematical symbols. Remind the children what < and > represent. Reinforce the idea that friction opposes and hence slows down movement.

Back at school
Mark the answers together. Compare results from the children's fair tests. Ask the children to set their own < and > questions for a quiz. **Answers:** true, false, false.

p112 Force report   LITERACY LINK

Learning objective
● To introduce the term *gravity* as the force which pulls things down.

Lesson context
Provide several objects such as a ball of Plasticine, a feather and a paper clip. Drop the Plasticine and ask what is making it fall. Elicit the word *gravity*. Ask the children to explore this by dropping the items in a fair test, observing how they fall and making annotated drawings.

Setting the homework
This activity invites the children to write a newspaper style report. Link the first picture story to the text, focusing on structure. Look at the second picture story together; make sure every child is clear about the role of force. Take suggestions for headlines.

Back at school

Ask children to read their reports. Compare the reports and look at a recent newspaper story, focusing on the format.
Answers: The force explanation should state that gravity pulls objects downwards.

p113 A game of two forces — SCIENCE TO SHARE

Learning objectives
- To know that air resistance can slow down the movement of objects.
- To know that a force acts in a particular direction and this can be represented by an arrow.

Lesson context
Demonstrate making a paper 'helicopter'. Brainstorm ideas on how it could be improved: weighting with paper clips, changing length of wings? Groups try these variables, measuring and recording the flight times.

Setting the homework
Discuss the air resistance observed. Demonstrate the principle of 'Blow Football'. Emphasise the need to use the straw safely.

Back at school
Ask the children to talk in groups about their matches and ideas. Ask each group to present its theories about air resistance, and reach a class consensus on its role.
Answers: arrow towards Sam as he breathes in, then away from him and down the straw; arrow away from Mags, meeting arrow from Sam, then travelling on.

p114 Sian's speedy skittles 2 — NUMERACY LINK

Learning objectives
- To present data in the form of a bar chart.
- To suggest explanations for their findings.

Lesson context
Show your class a table of science results. Model how to draw a bar chart. Ask the children to help you transfer the data. Ask questions about the chart. The children draw their own bar charts in groups, using data from other lessons.

Setting the homework
This activity links to the maths objective *collect and interpret data in graphs and tables*. The 'skittles' can be drinks cans, cartons or plastic bottles. Demonstrate the basic rules of bowling.

Back in school
Ask volunteers to present their work. The class can ask them about their results and how these compare with others' results. Compare and test predictions about how the scores will be affected by filling the skittles with water. Display the graphs. **Answers:** 5 skittles.

p115 Disappearing tricks — LITERACY LINK

Learning objectives
- To assess the children's knowledge and understanding of how forces can affect the shape and movement of objects.
- To assess the children's ability to plan a test, predict and suggest explanations.

Lesson context
This lesson allows the children to show what they have learned in this unit. Distribute blank paper and pictures

showing examples of forces at work. Ask questions about the pictures. Afterwards, gather the class together to share and discuss their answers.

Setting the homework
This is a pre-assessment or assessment task focusing on the science vocabulary from the unit. Play 'Definitions' in groups: one child finds a force word and gives the definition, the others try to guess the word. Make sure the children know what a wordsearch is.

Back at school
Mark the answers together. Play 'Definitions' with force words. Use the words from the sheet and the game to start a class dictionary. **Answers:** 2. friction, 3. Gravity, 4. Magnets, 5. newtons, 6. air, 7. result. Bonus word: prediction.

UNIT 7 LIGHT & SOUND — TRAVELLING AND REFLECTING

pp116-17 Trapped in the House of Doom! — SCIENCE TO SHARE

Learning objective
- To understand that the position of a shadow depends on the direction of the light source.

Lesson context
Point a torch (not switched on) at a Plasticine figure on a sheet of white paper. Where do the children think the shadow will fall? Draw the predictions on the sheet. With the torch on, ask a child to draw where the shadow falls and compare it to the predictions. Groups repeat the activity, using different figures and torch positions.

Setting the homework
Read through the script together. Talk about shadows in cartoons. Establish that details drawn on shadow puppets will not show up and why. Introduce the words *opaque* (the puppets) and *translucent* (the tissue paper). This activity requires planning from the children, and may be best suited to a holiday. The two A4 sheets can be copied onto an A3 sheet.

Back at school
Ask the children to show their puppets and any extra characters or scenery they created. Choose examples for a performance. Discuss the shadows made. **Answers:** The shadow is less clear when the torch is further away.

p118 How light travels — SCIENCE PRACTICE

Learning objectives
- To know that rays are reflected from surfaces.
- To observe closely.

Lesson context
Set up ray boxes making single and parallel rays. Use flat and curved surfaces and mirrors. Observe an image reflected from a curved surface, and how light reflected from a smooth surface will produce an image while light reflected from a rough surface will not.

Setting the homework
Talk about how we see objects when light enters our eyes. Demonstrate how to make a pinhole camera; emphasise that the hole must be tiny. Use the words *opaque* (black paper) and *translucent* (greaseproof paper).

Back at school

Ask the children to show their pinhole cameras and explain how they made them. Compare their pictures of the images they observed. Try out the cameras in groups. **Answers:** The image is upside down. Discuss why this is (because light travels in straight lines). Our eyes work the same way, but our brains correct the image to 'right way up'.

p119 Wake up, Grandma!   NUMERACY LINK

Learning objective
● To help children make connections with previous work on sound.

Lesson context

Ask your class to stand in a circle with their eyes closed and listen carefully for one minute. Ask them to describe the sounds and classify them as *loud* or *quiet* (or as *high* or *low*). Play a chime bar and ask the children how the sound gets to our ears. They can feel the vibration and try to change the sound, recording their ideas and findings.

Setting the homework

This activity links to interpreting pictograms with symbols for two or more units. Interpreting 'cold' data is a key skill for national tests. Discuss the sounds the children have heard, and remind them of graph scales used before.

Back at school

Groups compare the pictograms. Let the children use this approach for something they can participate in (such as TV programmes watched). **Answers:** shaker 12, cymbal 1, drum 2, whistle 4, bell 7; 3½ icons; 1. whistle, 2. two, 3. bell, 4. shaker, 5. cymbal.

p120 Which pitch?   SCIENCE PRACTICE

Learning objectives
● To recognise high and low pitch.
● To recognise that the pitch of a sound is related to the size of the vibrating part of an object.
● To notice patterns in their observations and make generalisations.

Lesson context

Hum a note and ask the children to join in. Make the note higher and lower. Discuss how we produce this sound. Use a xylophone to demonstrate different notes. Use the word *pitch*. Record the children's ideas about contrasting sounds.

Setting the homework

This activity allows the children to explore the concept of 'pitch' by making and listening to their own instruments. Remind them to measure accurately.

Back at school

Go through the test results. Make a collection of the children's explanations, and link this to the class work on vibration to reach a consensus. **Answers:** F, F, T; the explanation could refer to the length of ruler vibrating affecting the amount of air that vibrates.

p121 Cool vibes!   SCIENCE PRACTICE

Learning objectives
● To know that a larger vibrating body makes a louder sound.
● To make generalisations from the results of their own investigations.

Lesson context

Strike a tuning fork and place it in a tin to demonstrate how sound can be amplified. Repeat with different-sized containers, asking the children to predict how this will affect the sound's volume. Ask them to record predictions and results, then to agree on an '–er... –er' statement.

Setting the homework

This activity focuses on sound volume in terms of vibration. Remind the children to write accurate and clear notes.

Back at school

Explore the children's shaker drums. Ask for soft sounds, then louder, then softer. Focus on the movement of the rice; model how to write notes on this activity, using the children's suggestions. **Answers:** vibrations less; volume will increase; the harder the drum is hit, the greater the vibration, so the sound is louder.

p122 The sound of poetry   LITERACY LINK

Learning objective
● To apply knowledge and understanding of sound gained in previous lessons.

Lesson context

Ask the children to design and build musical instruments, using reclaimed materials. The instrument they make must produce more than one sound. Display the instruments; discuss the sounds they make, and whether the volume and pitch of the sound can be manipulated.

Setting the homework

The NLS in England encourages children to write poems based on personal experience. Focus on the children's science vocabulary and the context they have used it in during this unit.

Back at school

Encourage the children to read their poems aloud, varying the pitch and volume of their voices to suit the content. Use the poems for a class display or performance

UNIT 8 EARTH & BEYOND   THE SUN AND STARS

p123 Planet file   FINDING OUT

Learning objectives
● To elicit children's existing ideas about Earth and space.
● To stimulate question-raising.

Lesson context

Discuss what the children think the sky, Sun, Earth and Moon look like, encouraging comparisons with everyday objects. Groups use Plasticine to make models of the Earth, Sun and Moon. Ask them about the size and shapes of their models, then make a class list of 'Things we want to find out' (such as *Why do stars shine?*) Encourage questions that may not be answered in this unit, but stimulate interest.

Setting the homework

Talk about different sources of information that the children have used. Where are these services available locally?

Back at school

Ask the class to present their data files in groups, and to swap facts. Which information source was most useful to them? **Answers:** Only statements b and d are true.

p124 Escape from the StarTrap! NUMERACY LINK

Learning objectives
- To know that directions can be found using a compass.
- To use a compass to find north, south, east, west and mid-points between them, for example north-east.

Lesson context
Use a globe to identify north and south. Introduce west and east by discussing travel. Add the four compass points to a drawing of the UK. Go outside and identify the compass directions with a real compass. The children record the view in each direction, then plot routes to local landmarks using compass directions.

Setting the homework
This work has strong links to maths work on position and direction. Remind the children of the real compass and how they recorded routes.

Back at school
Discuss the homework. Ask the children to work out other routes (such as from Neptune Gate to the Space Scooter); record their ideas on a board or flip chart. **Answers:** Rahella is in the Jewel View Room; Zip and Zap can escape by going north-east, east, south-east, south-east, south-east (slight variations are possible).

p125 Sunset diary LITERACY LINK

Learning objectives
- To track the apparent movement of the Sun across the sky during the day.
- To carry out systematic observations over a period of time.

Lesson context
Observe the apparent movement of the Sun during the day by planting a stick in the playground and recording its shadow at regular intervals. Use a compass to record the direction the shadow is pointing in. Ask the children which direction the Sun is 'travelling' in. Discuss the results. Explain that the Earth moves, not the Sun.

Setting the homework
This activity links to report writing in literacy time. Talk about the seasons and consider the current season. Discuss the headings suggested for the report, looking at examples from previous work. Stress that the children must never look directly at the Sun.

Back at school
Compare the sunset diaries in groups. Collect the reports in a class report book for the school library.

p126 Shady days at the House of Doom NUMERACY LINK

Learning objective
- To investigate how shadows change when the angle of the Sun changes.

Lesson context
Using a torch and a variety of classroom objects, explore different ways of measuring a shadow: squared paper, ruler, measuring around it and so on. The children consider an investigation: altering the direction and angle of the light source and observing the shadows. Discuss how to make the test fair.

Setting the homework
This activity uses the maths skill of rounding positive integers to the nearest 10. Remind your class how to set out a bar chart with a title and labels. Stress that the bars in this chart should be separate, not touching.

Back in school
Compare some children's findings and graphs; encourage them to explain their answers. Talk through some rounding questions on a board or flip chart. Ask the children to set some for each other. Display the graphs. **Answers:** 80cm, 40cm, 70cm, 150cm; bar chart to show this data.

p127 Here comes the Sun SCIENCE PRACTICE

Learning objectives
- To know that the way the Sun heats the Earth depends on the slant of the Sun's rays.
- To measure temperature.

Lesson context
Recap on the Earth and Sun. Shine an anglepoise lamp onto a white card from directly above to represent summer. Change the angle of the light to represent autumn and winter (see diagram). Groups repeat the activity, using a thermometer to measure the temperature on the card.

Setting the homework
This activity relates our daily life to the Earth's rotation and orbit. Stress that approximate temperatures are valid if the children do not have access to a thermometer or weather report at home.

Back at school
Ask groups to look at each other's work. Each group should report back with most common and least common answers. Reach a class consensus. Display the pictures. **Answers:** Fact 1; Fact 3; without the Sun's light, the Earth would become very cold and nothing could survive here.

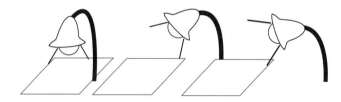

p128 Crazy Constellations SCIENCE TO SHARE

Learning objectives
- To know that a group of stars in the sky are known as constellations.
- To be able to identify some constellations.

Lesson context
Ask your class what they know about stars. Explain that some constellations (groups of stars) have been given names based on the shapes they made. Show photographs of the major constellations and ask the children to match them to a list of names. Can they think of new names? Remind them of dot-to-dot puzzles.

Setting the homework
Remind your class of the link between the shapes of the constellations and their names. Talk about making nets into 3-D shapes and demonstrate how to make a dice. Enlarge the sheet to A3 size.

Back at school
Play the game in groups. Introduce a bonus question based on this unit for each constellation.

Healthy eating

● Ask your helper whether you can help to write the weekly food shopping list.

● Write it here.

This week's food shopping:	

● Can you sort the foods in your shopping list into different kinds? Use this table to help you.

Energy-giving foods	Body-building foods	Maintenance foods

Do you think your family are eating a healthy, balanced diet? _____

Why do you think this? _____

_____

Dear Helper,

This activity will help your child to understand the importance of eating a healthy, balanced diet. Different foods are important for different reasons. We need some foods for activity and other foods for growth. Please involve your child in writing your weekly food shopping list, but please just write the things that you usually buy.

Health food café

Welcome to the Health Food Café.

- From our menu, choose two meals that you and a friend will enjoy.

- How much will each meal cost? Use these tables to work it out.

MENU
Starter

Fruit juice	50p
Vegetable soup	75p

Main course

Jacket potato	£1.50
Beans on toast	£1.40
Chicken salad	£1.75

Dessert

Fresh fruit salad	95p
Yoghurt	50p

Name:

Items	Cost
Total	

Name:

Items	Cost
Total	

- How much will you spend altogether?

_____

- How much change would you get from £10?

_____

- Use this space for your working out.

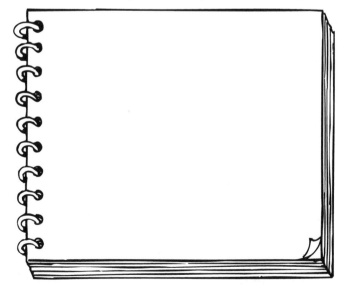

Dear Helper,

This activity is part of some science work on healthy eating. Encourage your child to create two different meals from the choices on the menu. Also, encourage them to use the space provided for working out the bill and the change. Working out problems like this on paper is an important skill, so please ask your child to write their maths work in the space and leave it there.

■ SCHOLASTIC

TEETH AND FOOD (**OURSELVES** (**UNIT 1**)

Growing up

An **autobiography** is a book someone has written to tell the story of his or her own life.

● Use these questions to help you start your own autobiography. You may need to ask your family and friends for some of the answers.

What was the date and time of your birth?	
Where were you born?	
How much did you weigh at birth?	
How big were you at birth?	
What were your favourite toys as a baby?	
When did you first sleep all night?	
What were your favourite foods as a baby?	
When did you first walk?	
How tall are you now?	
How much do you weigh now?	

● Now write about yourself and how you have grown. Continue on the back of this sheet if necessary.

Dear Helper,

Children often like to write about themselves. Please help your child by giving them the basic information for this table. Feel free to write the answers in the table for your child. Encourage your child to write their own 'autobiography' in clear sentences, with capital letters and full stops, and to read out what they have written to you.

Amazing teeth

Teeth are truly amazing. You have learned some facts about different kinds of teeth. But there are lots of other things to find out. Did you know that the hardest part of your body is the surface of your teeth?

● Can you find out any more amazing facts about teeth? They could be about our teeth or the teeth of animals – it's up to you. You could use books or CD-ROMs, or look on the Internet. If you can use the Internet, try this website: www.aquafresh.co.uk (join the Kids' Club).

● Write your amazing facts inside this tooth.

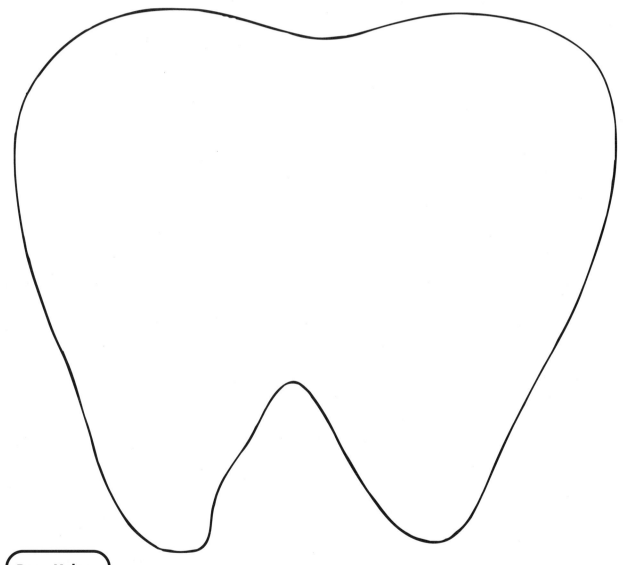

Dear Helper,

This activity continues your child's work on teeth as an aspect of ourselves. Please help your child to find some interesting facts about teeth, using encyclopedias, the library or the Internet. You could also try the website http://kids-world.colgatepalmolive.com (join the No Cavities Club) and www.dentalhealth.org.uk/ funbit/didyknow.htm (you will need to choose facts suitable for your child from this site). As with all work of this kind, your child should try to express the facts in their own words, not just copy out what they find.

Name:

Taking care of teeth

● What can you do to take care of your teeth?
Write down three things and why they will help.

Things you should do	Why?

● Read about these three children. Which child do you think will have the most trouble with his or her teeth? Why?

| **Name:** Sally

Eats: lots of sweets

Cleans teeth: after eating sweets | **Name:** Rehan

Eats: lots of fresh fruit and vegetables

Cleans teeth: at least twice a day | **Name:** Pierre

Eats: lots of chocolate biscuits

Cleans teeth: sometimes |

I think _____ will have the most trouble with his/her

teeth because _____

_____

Dear Helper,

Looking after our teeth is very important. Your child has been learning about how to look after their teeth. Please talk with your child about this. Encourage them to think of three really important things. They need to think about what we should not eat, what we should do to help ourselves, and who can help us to care for our teeth.

Making sense

Our senses tell us about the world around us. Can you remember what

our senses are called, and which parts of our bodies we use to sense with?

Think about what life would be like without our senses. What would you miss most?

● Fill in this table.

Name of a sense	The body part that we use for this sense	Things I could not do without this sense	The things I would miss the most

Mr Fergs' wordsearch

Living things have seven characteristics
that separate them from non-living things.

● Find the words that make **Mr Fergs** in the grid and write them below.

R	N	S	F	G	W	I	N	D	E	Z	S
M	O	V	E	M	E	N	T	A	L	M	E
O	I	G	E	H	E	T	Y	U	B	X	N
U	T	F	D	V	B	I	R	D	A	H	S
S	A	I	I	Q	T	X	A	Y	T	Q	I
E	R	S	N	Y	W	R	C	H	J	B	T
Y	I	H	G	R	O	W	T	H	U	O	I
U	P	L	A	N	T	O	F	R	H	O	V
P	S	T	T	Q	H	P	E	R	G	K	I
O	E	X	C	R	E	T	I	O	N	Y	T
D	R	D	L	P	Y	H	Q	J	V	Q	Y
R	E	P	R	O	D	U	C	T	I	O	N

(The words may go
across or down.)

M _ _ _ _ _ _ _ _

R _ _ _ _ _ _ _ _ _ _

F _ _ _ _ _ _

E _ _ _ _ _ _ _ _ _

R _ _ _ _ _ _ _ _ _

G _ _ _ _ _

S _ _ _ _ _ _ _ _ _ _

● Also in the grid are the names of four living things and
four non-living things. Find them and write them below.

Living	Non-living

Dear Helper,

Your child has been learning about the seven characteristics of living things. When they have found the
seven words in the grid, ask them what each word means. When they have found the names of the living
and non-living things, ask them to explain why these things are not living.

Movement survey

● Carry out a survey of the different ways that animals move. You could look around your garden, or investigate a local park with an adult. Use this table to keep a tally mark record of your survey.

Ways of moving	Number of animals seen	Total
Walking upright		
Walking on four legs		
Swimming		
Crawling		
Sliding		
Hopping		
Running		
Flying		

● Now draw a bar chart to show your results.

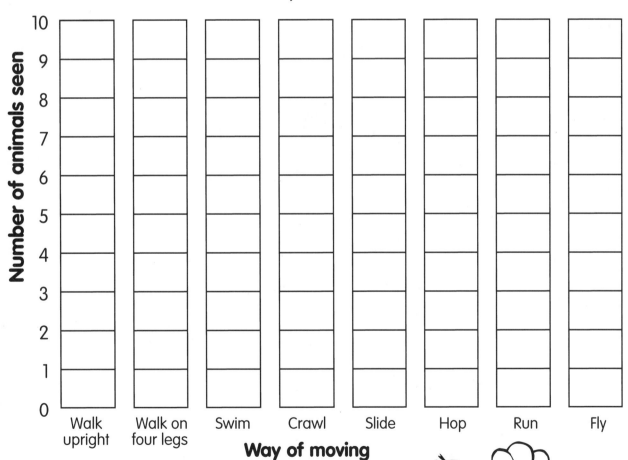

Way of moving

Dear Helper,

In this activity, your child is asked to make a survey of how animals move. Please make sure that they do this from a safe place. Encourage them to record what they see using tally marks (such as ⧸⧸⧸⧸⧸), and then to write the total as digits (such as 5). If your child cannot explore outside, let them look in books for pictures of animals on the move.

Name:

Animal senses

Animals use their senses to know what is happening around them. Do you know which parts of their bodies animals use for their senses?

● Draw a line to match each body part with the animal it belongs to. Next to each animal picture, write down which sense the animal is using.

Sense

_____

_____

_____

_____

_____

● Try this animal senses crossword. When you have filled it in, you should see another word running down the centre.

1. Rabbits twitch this.

2. Owls have large ones.

3. An animal uses this to taste.

4. Animals sense being touched with this.

5. An animal's senses warn it about this.

6. Rabbits have floppy ones.

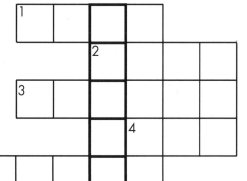

Dear Helper,

This activity continues some work on animal senses. Please help your child by talking about the sense organs of various animals (such as eyes and ears), and how these help to make animals aware of what is happening around them.

Little and large

Sometimes the word used for a young animal is a completely different word from the parent's name. Sometimes it is made by adding a suffix (a special ending) to the parent's name.

● Use the ten names in the box to write the correct name of the young animal next to each animal name in the list below.

cub	kitten	calf	puppy	tadpole
kid	chick	child	cub	lamb

1. bear _____

2. hen _____

3. cat _____

4. dog _____

5. lion _____

6. sheep _____

7. cow _____

8. human _____

9. frog _____

10. goat _____

● Now try these. This time you need to remove a suffix from the end of the young animal's name to make the name of the parent animal.

1. duckling _____

2. spiderling _____

3. owlet _____

4. piglet _____

● Now try these. You may need to look in books for the correct names.

1. cygnet _____

2. leveret _____

3. fawn _____

4. grub _____

Dear Helper,

As part of our work on animals, your child has been learning about young animals. This activity develops your child's vocabulary by looking at names of the young. Your child may need some help with the last section. Encourage them to use dictionaries or reference books to find the names.

■ SCHOLASTIC

Name:

Food from plants

Does most of your food come from plants,

or does it come from animals?

● Look in your cupboards at home. Write on the leaves of this plant the names of foods that come from plants or are made from plants (such as corn flakes).

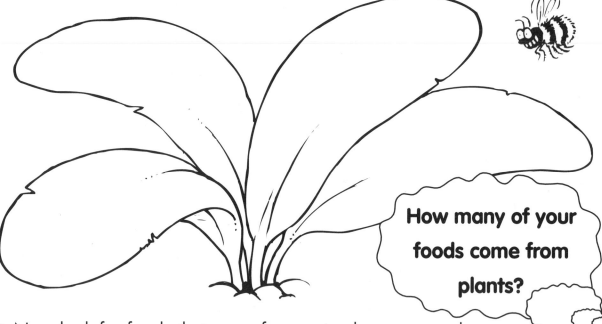

How many of your foods come from plants?

● Now look for foods that come from animals or are made from animals (such as fish paste). Write the names of those foods here.

How many of your foods come from animals?

Dear Helper,

In this activity, your child is asked to look at the different kinds of food at home. Please help them to make a list and sort the foods into two groups: those that come from plants and those that come from animals. Some, such as margarine or butter, may need some explanation.

Name:

Looking at roots

You will need: a clean jar (such as a jam or coffee jar); a sheet of blotting paper to fit into the jar; water; 6–8 dried peas or beans.

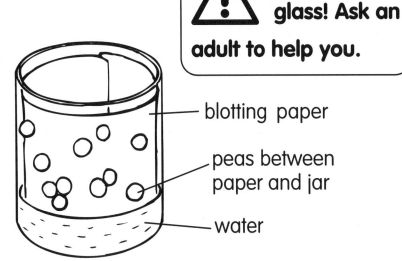

Take care with glass! Ask an adult to help you.

blotting paper

peas between paper and jar

water

What to do:

● Line the jar with blotting paper.

● Place the peas in between the jar and the paper.

● Put some water in the jar so that the bottom of the paper is wet.

● Top up the water every day.

● Draw pictures to record how the pea roots grow over the next 14 days. When you have filled in the spaces below, use the back of this sheet.

Day 1	Day 2
Day 3	Day 4
Day 5	Day 6

Dear Helper,

This activity will encourage your child to watch how a plant's roots develop from a seed – something they cannot normally see when seeds are planted in soil or compost. Encourage your child to top up the water in the jar and sketch what they see every day for a fortnight. It might be easier to focus on the growth of just one plant. Discuss why plants need roots: to take in water and (normally) to hold them in the ground.

PHOTOCOPIABLE

📖SCHOLASTIC

Name:

At the garden centre

● Visit a garden centre or the gardening section of a DIY store. Look at the plants and read some of the information given about them.

● Sometimes the plants are arranged so that you can choose plants for particular conditions: sunny or shady, damp or dry. Write down what you find out about the special conditions that some plants need to grow well.

GARDEN CENTRE
PLANTS FOR ALL CONDITIONS

Plant name	Grows well in...

Dear Helper,

Different plants need different conditions to grow well. If possible, take your child to visit a garden centre or DIY store, so that they can identify plants that grow in particular conditions. Encourage and help your child to look for plants that grow well in conditions such as *sunny* or *shady* or *damp*. At this stage, it is best not to talk about soil types. Plants in a garden centre may be arranged by the conditions they need, or have labels with icons such as ✸ for 'needs sunlight'. If a visit to such a place is not possible, most gardening books have sections on plants that grow better in sunlight or in shade.

World environments

There are many different environments across the world. Here are four of them: a desert, a polar region, a rainforest and an ocean.

● Fill in the gaps in this table. Draw a picture to show the main things in each environment.

Description	Place	Picture
I am a very hot place. I am very dry. Nothing much grows here.	I am a _____	
I am a very hot place. I am often very wet. Lots of plants and animals live here.	I am a _____	
	I am a polar region.	
	I am an ocean.	

Dear Helper,

In this activity, your child is identifying the main features of different environments across the world. Encourage them to draw illustrations that show features such as the landscape, the weather and the plants and animals that live there.

Voyage of discovery

● Imagine you are taking part in an expedition to a faraway place to find out what animals and plants live there. You can choose from: a desert, the North or South Pole, a rainforest or an ocean. Write a diary to record what happens, and particularly the things you find each day.

● When you have filled in the diary page below, you can write on the back of this sheet.

Day 1

_____

_____

_____

_____

Day 2

_____

_____

_____

_____

Day 3

_____

_____

_____

_____

Day 4

_____

_____

_____

_____

Day 5

_____

_____

_____

_____

Day 6

_____

_____

_____

_____

Dear Helper,

This activity continues our work in class relating to different environments in the world and the plants and animals that live there. Please encourage your child to think carefully about their chosen environment, describe it and write about the plants and animals they might find. A visit to the local library may help your child to find some background detail, but is not essential.

Name: _____

Who lives there?

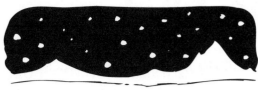

● Find out the names of some animals that usually live in each of these environments.

Polar regions	Rainforests	Oceans	Deserts

● Think about one animal that lives in each environment. Can you explain what is special about it that helps it to live there? We say this is how animals are **adapted** to live in a particular place.

Polar regions   Animal: _____

How it is adapted: _____

Rainforests   Animal: _____

How it is adapted: _____

Oceans   Animal: _____

How it is adapted: _____

Deserts   Animal: _____

How it is adapted: _____

Dear Helper,

This activity will encourage your child to carry out some research into the plants and animals living in these places. Reference books and the Internet could be useful sources of information. Perhaps you could visit your local library together.

Habitats

Some plants and animals usually live in

light places, others usually live in dark places.

● Where do these living things usually live?
   Complete this table by ticking the correct boxes for each plant or animal.
   You don't need to answer all three questions for each plant or animal.

Plant or animal	Light or dark?		Dry or damp?		Hot or cold?	
Woodlouse						
Cactus						
Moss						
Earthworm						
Snail						
Sunflower						

● Can you think of another two examples?

Dear Helper,

This activity backs up the class work on habitats. Please encourage your child to think carefully about the conditions needed by each animal or plant. The questions in the table can sometimes be left unanswered, since the choice does not always make a difference to the plant or animal.

How much waste?

Have you ever thought about how much waste or rubbish we produce at home? A lot of it can be recycled and used again.

● Over a week, carefully find **either** the mass of paper **or** the mass of plastic bottles that could be recycled.

Day	Mass of paper	Mass of plastic bottles
Sunday		
Monday		
Tuesday		
Wednesday		
Thursday		
Friday		
Saturday		
Total		

Some children have been saving and weighing their waste paper.

The results are shown in this bar chart.

Claire — Carlos — Ayesha — Tom — Pat

Weight in kg: 1, 2, 3, 4, 5

Who collected the most paper? _____

How much paper did Pat collect? _____

How much paper did the children collect altogether? _____

Dear Helper,

This maths activity is designed to raise your child's awareness of the amount of waste in our homes that can be recycled. Encourage your child to carry out this task each day. ⚠ **Make sure that any paper or plastic bottles collected are clean and safe before your child weighs them.**

Don't waste it, recycle it!

- Talk with your parent or carer about recycling.

- Make a list of types of waste in the home that could be recycled.

- Design a poster to persuade people to recycle the waste in their homes, such as paper, glass and plastic.

Dear Helper,

Only a very small percentage of the everyday waste that could be recycled is actually recycled. As part of our work on waste in the environment, your child has been thinking about how people can be persuaded to recycle. Please encourage your child with this activity: help them to think through the main issues, and to come up with a catchy slogan and an attractive design.

Inside my house

- On another sheet of paper, draw a picture of one of the rooms in your home – perhaps your bedroom. Use your senses of touch and sight to identify the materials that some things are made of. Add labels to your picture, such as this:

The window frames are made from wood.

walls   door   window
frame   pieces of furniture

- Here are some things to show in your picture:

- Add some other interesting items, such as favourite toys or games.

- Now complete this table:

Name of the item	Which material is it made from?	Which of your senses did you use?	Why do you think this material was used?

Dear Helper,

Your child has been looking at how different materials are used. This activity encourages them to use their senses to identify different materials in the home. Please help them to identify what materials have been used to make the objects they have drawn: wood, glass, plastic, paper and so on. Encourage them to ask why certain materials are used for particular purposes.

Now and then

The ways that things are made have changed over the years. Often, new materials are used.

● Talk to an adult who can remember what some of these things were like when they were young, and what they were made from.

Object	Old material	New material

One material has replaced many others. Which one? _____

Dear Helper,

In this activity, your child has to find out how the materials that we use for making things have changed. Please encourage your child by talking with them about the objects on the sheet, or by helping to contact older relatives who can remember further back. For example, a great-grandparent might remember milk in pails delivered by a horse-drawn dray.

Name:

Material adjectives

Nouns are the names of things. Adjectives are words that describe things. For example, in 'rusty iron', **iron** is a noun (the name of the material) and **rusty** is an adjective.

● Think of some good adjectives to describe these nouns. They are all the names of different materials.

Paper

Wood

Glass

Plastic

Stone

Dear Helper,

In science, it is important to use words carefully and exactly. This activity encourages the use of adjectives (describing words) to talk about the features of different materials. Encourage your child to think of interesting adjectives.

Natural or manufactured?

Some materials that we use, such as wood, are **natural**. That means they come from the world around us. Other materials, such as plastic, are **manufactured**. That means people have made them from other materials.

● Sort these materials into two groups: natural and manufactured. Can you think of some more materials of each kind?

wool   plastic   glass   wood   cotton   paper   polystyrene   stone

Natural or processed	Manufactured

● Choose two of these materials, one natural and one manufactured. Use books or the Internet to find out more about them.

Name of material		
Is it natural?	natural	manufactured
Where does it come from or how is it made?		
What is it used for?		
Other useful facts about this material		

Dear Helper,

Your child has been looking at the materials things are made from, and how some materials are natural and others are manufactured. This activity encourages your child to find out more about how we obtain and use natural and manufactured materials. Please help by taking your child to visit the library, or assisting with an Internet search if you have access to a computer.

Name:

Rocks

- Collect some different-sized stones and rocks from one place. Six will be enough – nothing too big! Make sure they are fairly clean. Try to find some different types of rock or stone.

- Put your stones in order of mass, the smallest first, just by looking at them. Number them and sketch them, then estimate the mass of each stone.

- Use scales to find the actual mass of each stone. Fill in the table below.

Sketch of rock	Estimated mass (g)	Actual mass (g)
1.		
2.		
3.		
4.		
5.		
6.		

What is the total mass of your rock collection? _____

Dear Helper,

This maths-linked activity develops science work on looking at different types of rock. Encourage your child to make a collection of rocks – but not to collect too many! The use of some kitchen scales would be very helpful, but your child may need to be shown how to use them.

⚠ **Please make sure that your child washes the rocks and keeps the scales clean!**

Soil

The soil in your garden has been made over millions of years.

● What is it like? Collect some in a jar or a tray. Look at it and feel it.

● Draw a sketch of your soil in the box below. Include stones and any minibeasts you see.

● Now think of some words to describe the soil in your garden. Write your words around the outside of the box.

● Remember to wash your hands when you have finished handling the soil.

Dear Helper,

This activity supports the class work your child has been doing on rocks and soils. Soil is a mixture of crushed rock, decaying plants and water. Help your child to observe the soil carefully, and ask them to explain how the different parts of soil came to be there.

⚠ **Please make sure that your child washes their hands after touching soil.**

Sidebar: MATERIALS UNIT 4 · NATURAL AND MANUFACTURED MATERIALS · PHOTOCOPIABLE

There's a fault here!

● Look very carefully at these pictures. Can you see four things in each picture that would break an Electrical Safety Code? Circle each one.

● On the back of this sheet, write a slogan about using electricity safely.

Dear Helper,

Electrical safety is a very important aspect of any work related to electricity. Your child is learning about electricity and how it is used, including the importance of safety. Please encourage your child to consider these issues. Emphasise that while they can handle batteries and bulbs in class, it is not safe to use mains electricity in the same way because the power is much stronger.

Name:

Writing instructions

● Write step-by-step instructions to tell someone how to make a simple circuit with a battery, a bulb, a buzzer and a switch. Think about the instructions you get with new toys or games. Include diagrams. Give each step a number.

Dear Helper,

This activity reinforces work in school on making simple electrical circuits. Please encourage your child to write a set of instructions in clear, logical steps. They should not assume that the reader knows anything about electricity.

Name: _____

Broken circuits

● Which of these four circuits will **not** allow electricity to flow? Put a tick in the box for each complete circuit. Put a cross for each broken circuit.

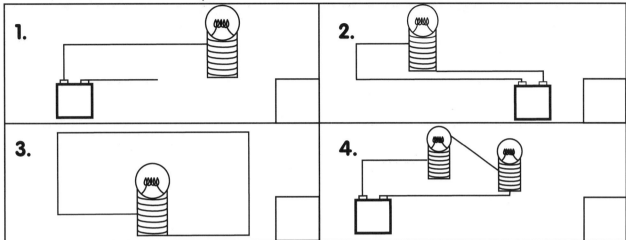

● Now draw some different circuits.

Broken	Complete

● Explain what things are needed to make a complete circuit. _____
_____

Dear Helper,

In class, your child has been looking at and making complete circuits. A circuit has to be complete for electricity to flow round it. It is important for your child to be able to see whether a circuit is complete or not. Please encourage your child by talking about each of the diagrams. Work through their own suggestions, checking that they have drawn broken and complete circuits.

Morse code

We use Morse code to send messages using sound or light. This is how we write it:

A . –	B – . . .	C – . – .	D – . .	E .	F . . – .
G – – .	H	I . .	J . – – –	K – . –	L . – . .
M – –	N – .	O – – –	P . – – .	Q – – . –	R . – .
S . . .	T –	U . . –	V . . . –	W . – –	X – . . –
Y – . – –	Z – – . .				

1 . – – – –	2 . . – – –	3 . . . – –	4 . . . . –	5 . . . . .
6 –	7 – – . . .	8 – – – . .	9 – – – – .	10 – – – – –

● Write a simple message in words, then write it in Morse code.
Send it to your helper in Morse code, using a torch.

Message in words: _____

Coded message: _____

● Now ask your helper to send a different message to you.
Write it down in Morse code, then decode it into words.

Coded message: _____

Decoded message: _____

● Who do you think used to send messages using Morse code?

_____

Dear Helper,

Electricity is used to communicate in many ways. Your child has been looking at the Morse code as a means of communicating by sounds or flashes of light. Please let your child send a Morse code message to you, then send a message back to them. If you don't have a torch, you could clap or hum the message.

Name:

Communication survey

The methods we all use to keep in touch with each other are called **communication systems**. Most of them use electricity.

● The table below shows three communication systems that use electricity. Can you think of some more?

● Do a survey to find out how many of them you have at home.

Communication system	Do you have any at home?	How many do you have?
Television 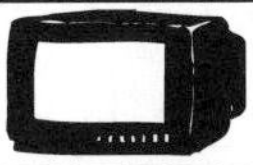		
Radio 		
Telephone (fixed) 		

Which communication system do you have the greatest number of?

_____

If you had to manage without one system, which one would it be?

_____

Explain your choice. _____

_____

Dear Helper,

We use electricity to communicate all the time in everyday life. This activity asks your child to carry out a survey of all the communication devices there are in the home. Please help them to find all the appropriate pieces of equipment, and encourage them to use the correct name for each one.

What's on the TV?

Electricity is used not only when we watch television, but also when the programmes are made.

3:30	**Children's TV** – all your favourites
5:30	**Quiz Time** – pit your wits against the contestants
6:00	**World News**
6:30	**Local News**
6:45	**The Service Station** – NEW drama!
7:30	**World Tiddlywinks Championships** – further live coverage
8:30	**Kitchen Force** – another makeover for a weary cook
9:00	**World News**
9:30	**Local News**
9:45	**Weather Watch**
10:00	**The Toast Smugglers** – late movie

● This evening's TV schedule is shown opposite. Read it carefully, then answer the questions below.

1. Which programme begins at 5:30? _____

2. How long does **Children's TV** go on for? _____

3. If you switched on at 7:45, which programme would you see? _____

4. If you watched **Quiz Time** and **Kitchen Force**, how long would you have watched TV for? _____

5. Which is the only programme to last for exactly 60 minutes? _____

6. If you switched on at 8.45, how long would you have to wait for the **World News** to begin? _____

Dear Helper,

This activity is linked to maths work. It encourages your child to solve real-life problems involving time. Please support and encourage your child by helping them to read the questions and find the answers (work out the answers by talking, not on paper). You could also ask similar questions using TV listings in magazines or newspapers.

Push or pull?

When the poles of two magnets are placed close together, the magnetic force between them either pulls them together or pushes them apart.

● Decide what will happen to each pair of magnets. Write **pushed** or **pulled** next to each pair.

N S	N S	_____
N S	S N	_____
S N	N S	_____
S N	S N	_____

● Which words do we use to describe these pushes and pulls? Complete each of these sentences with a word from the box below.

A pull by a magnet is called _____.

A push by a magnet is called _____.

Like poles _____.

Unlike poles _____.

attract	repulsion	repel	attraction

● Draw some different magnets with some small pins sticking to them.

Dear Helper,

When magnets are brought together, the magnetic forces between them either push or pull the magnets. This activity backs up school work on magnets and the science words used to describe magnetic pushes and pulls. Your child may need some help with the correct use of these words. Perhaps you could look them up in a dictionary together.

Name:

The Great Magnet Game

● Look at the objects in 'The Great Magnet Game'. Write under each object the material it is usually made from. Use the list of materials in this box:

> **steel   wood   paper   glass   plastic**

THE GREAT MAGNET GAME

● Now circle the objects in the Great Magnet Game that are attracted by magnets. If you have a magnet at home, you could check your answers.

● Think about the materials that these objects are made from. Which of the materials are magnetic and which are not? Write them in this table. You can add some more materials of your own.

Materials attracted by magnets	Materials not attracted by magnets

Dear Helper,

This activity continues our class work on materials that are attracted by magnets. These are iron and steel (although stainless steel is not magnetic). If you have a magnet, encourage your child to test real objects for attraction – but please remind them not to put magnets near cassette tapes, computer disks or TV sets.

Name:

Jack in the Box

● With your helper, use this sheet to make a Jack in the Box. Decorate the parts before you make the box.

You will need: coloured pens or pencils, scissors, paper glue or sticky tape.

What to do:

1. Decorate the box net and the 'Jack'.

2. Cut out the box net. Use glue or tape on the shaded tabs to stick the box together. Leave the lid free to open.

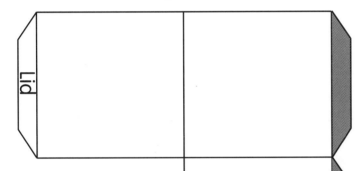

Glue or tape the shaded tabs.

Glue or tape together.

3. Cut out the 'Jack'. Fold the paper strip in a zigzag to make a spring.

4. Glue or tape the bottom of the spring to the floor of the box.

5. Gently push the spring down and shut the lid on the 'Jack'.

6. Lift the lid and watch the 'Jack' spring up.

Glue or tape to floor of box.

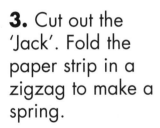

Dear Helper,

This activity supports school work on forces and springs. Please talk with your child about why the Jack jumps up when the lid is lifted. Your child may need some help with making the box and the Jack.

■ SCHOLASTIC

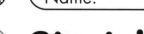

Stretchy elastic

● Use an elastic band to make a simple force meter.

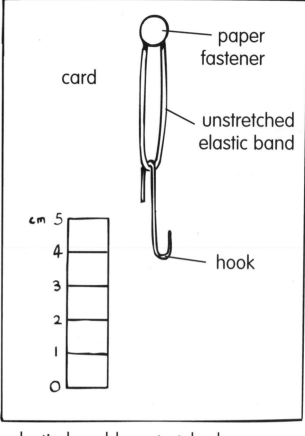

card

paper fastener

unstretched elastic band

hook

Instructions

1. Cut out a piece of card 15cm × 10cm. An old birthday card or cereal packet would be ideal.

2. Use a paper fastener to fix an elastic band to the card.

3. Straighten a paper clip into a hook shape. Hang it from the elastic band.

4. Mark a scale on the card in cm.

To use the force meter:

Hold the card at the top and hang a small object (such as a key) on the hook. Read the scale to see how far the elastic band has stretched.

● Now use your force meter to see how far the elastic band will stretch when you hang different objects on the hook.

Do not try anything too big or heavy.

Object	Length of elastic band

● What do you notice from the results of your investigation?

_____

_____

Dear Helper,

Your child has been thinking about how the force applied to an elastic band affects the amount of stretch. In this activity, your child is asked to make a simple force meter (the stretch of the elastic band provides a rough measure of force). Please help your child to construct the force meter. Make sure they do not try to test any items that are too heavy for the elastic band to support.

Vehicle building

You have already built a simple four-wheeled vehicle. Can you tell someone else how to build one?

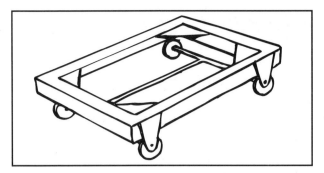

● Write a set of instructions to help someone build a model vehicle. You may want to include drawings.

Materials you need:
Tools you need:
How to build the model:

Dear Helper,

As part of our work on forces, your child has built a simple model of a four-wheeled vehicle in class. Please ask your child to tell you about the model and how they made it. Encourage them to describe all the steps in the right order. This will help them to think clearly about what they did before writing a set of instructions to help someone else make the same model.

Name:

Energy and fuel

Appliances are things that use an energy source

to do something useful. They change energy from one form to another.

For example, a heater might change electrical energy to heat energy.

● Look around your home at some of the appliances you have. Fill in this table to show the energy they use and the energy they produce.

Appliance (picture)	Energy used	Energy produced

● Now use reference books or the Internet to find out how **one** of these was formed: coal, gas or oil. Write on the back of this sheet.

Dear Helper,

This activity continues our work on energy by looking at how household appliances change energy from one form to another. Your child is also asked to find out how one type of fuel was formed. Please help them to find this information.

Me and my shadow

Imagine your shadow came to life and you made friends with it. Can you describe it? Was it like you or different?

- Write a list of adjectives to describe your shadow.

- Now make a storyboard with pictures and words to show an adventure that you and your shadow had. Remember what you need to make shadows.

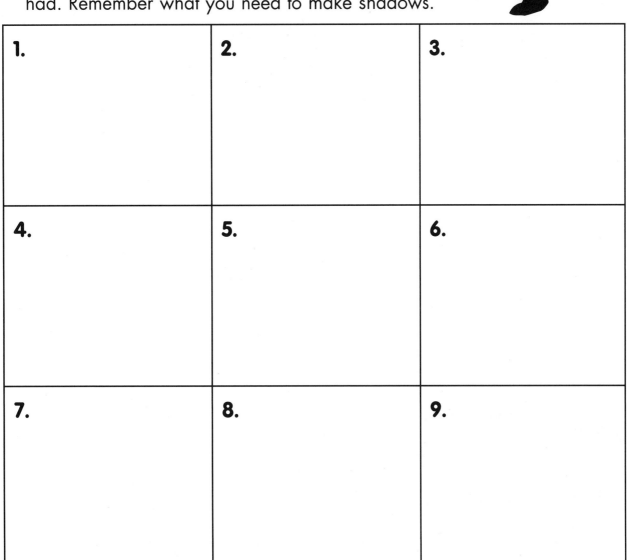

1.	2.	3.
4.	5.	6.
7.	8.	9.

Dear Helper,

In class, we are exploring how shadows are made when light is blocked. Shadows are all around us. They can change in shape and size when an object or a light source moves. Please encourage your child to think about this as they write their storyboard, which is a plan for a further piece of creative writing. (A storyboard is a series of pictures with captions, like an old-fashioned comic strip.)

Name:

Light sources

● Think about the different things that provide us with light in different places. For each situation, write down as many light sources as you can think of.

At home:	During a power cut:
On a camping holiday:	**In the street at night:**

● Some bright objects are light sources, but some are just reflecting light. Fill in this table by ticking the correct column for each object.

Object	Light source	Reflects light
A star		
Clothes		
The Sun		
A fire		
The Moon		
A book		
The TV		
A candle		

Dear Helper,

This activity reinforces work on sources of light. A light source can be either natural (such as the Sun) or manufactured (such as a torch). Light sources produce their own light, but everything else that we see is just reflecting light. The Moon is just reflecting sunlight. Please help your child by encouraging them to think carefully about the different light sources we use.

Name:

Car colour survey

Don't go near the roadside. Carry out your survey from a safe place.

- Carry out a survey to find out which colour of car is the most popular.
- Keep a tally to record how many cars of each colour you see in 15 minutes. For example: red ~~||||~~

Colour	Tally count	Colour	Tally count

- Now make a bar chart to show the five most popular colours.

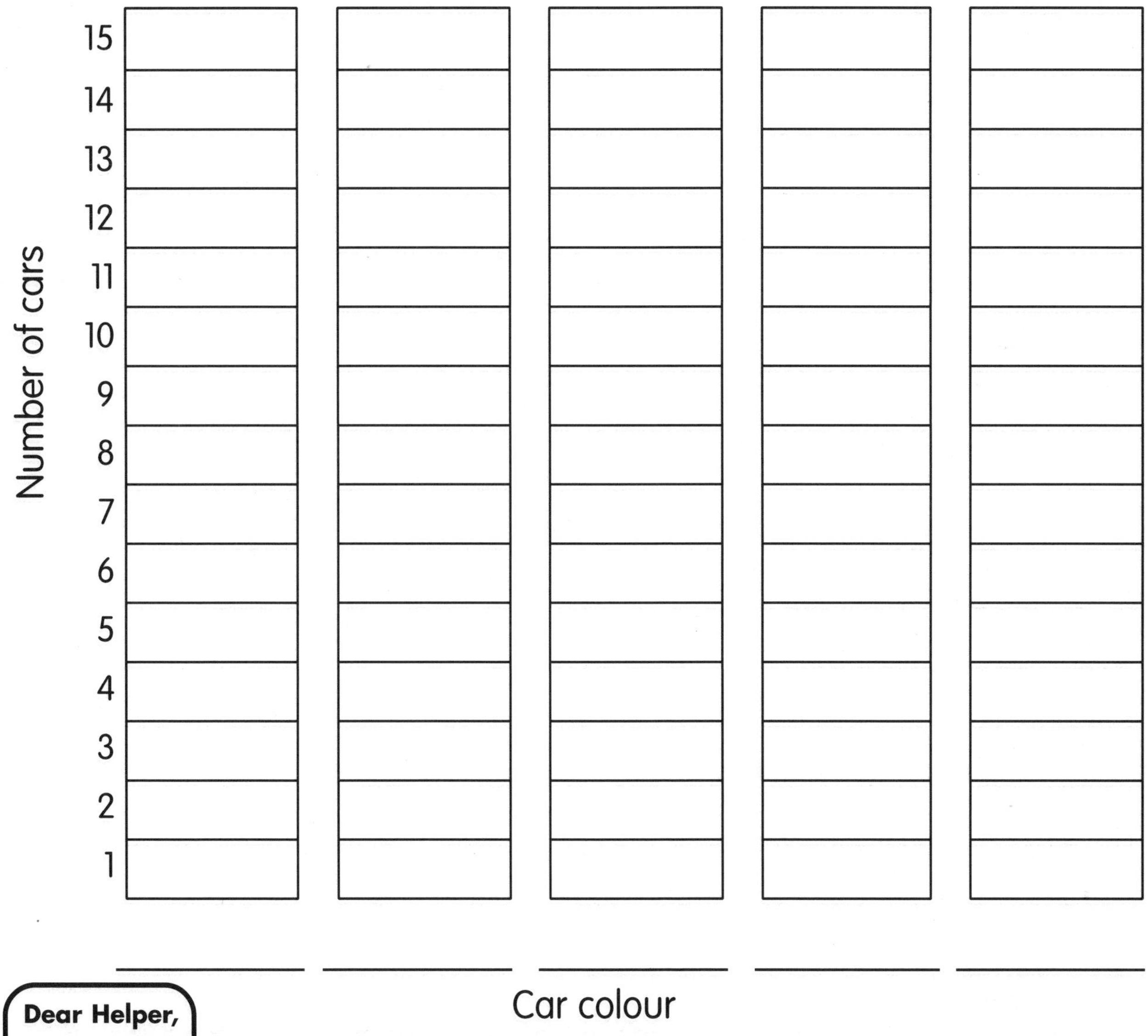

Number of cars
15
14
13
12
11
10
9
8
7
6
5
4
3
2
1
Car colour

Dear Helper,

This activity requires your child to carry out a survey of the car colours seen going past a particular place over 15 minutes. The information should be recorded in a tally chart before being transferred to the bar chart. **It is essential that you help to make sure this survey is done safely. Thank you.**

SOURCES AND EFFECTS (LIGHT & SOUND UNIT 7)

Musical instruments

● Find out all you can about one musical instrument. It could be a woodwind, percussion, brass, stringed or keyboard instrument. Use reference books or the Internet to find out how the instrument is played, what it is made from and how large it is. Draw the instrument. Write some interesting facts around your picture.

Dear Helper,

Your child has been investigating the variety of sounds that can be made, and the sources of these sounds. Musical instruments are very useful for exploring sounds. Please help your child to find out about one particular instrument – especially how it is used to make sounds. If your child plays an instrument, concentrate on that one.

PHOTOCOPIABLE

Making music

● Design and make a simple musical instrument using 'junk' materials such as plastic bottles, jars and cardboard boxes. It could be something that you hit, pluck, blow or shake. It could play only one note or many different notes – it's up to you and your helper. Please ask before you take any bottles or boxes!

● Draw your ideas here before you make the instrument.

● Write a list of the materials you used.

Dear Helper,

Some sounds are loud, others are soft. Some have a high pitch, others a low pitch. Musical instruments can produce all different kinds of sounds. Please help your child to make a simple instrument from junk materials and explore the sounds that can be made with it. Encourage them to design their instrument first rather than just going ahead and making it.

ゑSCHOLASTIC

Name:

Sound words

We often recognise things by the sounds they make.

Animals make special sounds, such as the moo of a cow.

Some objects make special sounds, such as the tick of a clock.

● Can you match the sounds in this box to the things listed below?
Write the correct sound next to each animal or object.

slam	bleat	meow	clatter	patter
growl	beat	creak	neigh	roar

1. Lions _____

2. Doors _____

3. Lambs _____

4. Hinges _____

5. Horses _____

6. Raindrops _____

7. Cats _____

8. Drums _____

9. Bears _____

10. Hoofs _____

● Now write an **acrostic poem** about one of these animals or objects.
Your poem should describe the sounds it makes. Here is an example:

Calling softly in the night

A cat meows

To tell the world that

Supper is in sight.

● Write your poem on another sheet of paper. Work on it until it is finished.
Then write it neatly on the back of this sheet.

Dear Helper,

As part of our work in science, we have been thinking about sounds. This activity encourages your child to think about the words we use to describe the sounds that some animals and objects make. Please help your child by discussing these words. When your child is writing the acrostic poem, encourage them to draft their work before writing out the final version.

Shadow puppets

● Make a shadow puppet by cutting out a shape from card (for example, a cereal box). The puppet can look like anything, but keep it simple. For example, you could draw around your hand to make a shadow puppet. Stick your shape onto a short stick such as a pencil. You will also need a light source such as a torch.

● Make a shadow with the puppet. What do you think will happen to the shadow if you move it nearer to the light source, then away from the light source?

● Draw pictures to show what happened.

My shadow puppet

Shadow when puppet is nearer to the light	Shadow when puppet is further from the light

Dear Helper,

This activity backs up class work on shadows. Your child may need some help with making the shadow puppet. Please talk with your child about the shadows that it makes. Encourage them to make different-sized shadows by moving the puppet and the light source.

Shadow lengths

You will need: four small objects, a ruler or tape measure, a sunny day.

● Choose four small things from around your home. Measure how high each object is. When there is enough sunlight to make good shadows, measure how long each object's shadow is. Remember to measure carefully and accurately.

Object	Height of object (cm)	Length of shadow (cm)

● Now draw a bar graph to show your results. Colour in a bar for each object and fill in its shadow with black. Label the objects and the units.

Dear Helper,

In this activity, your child is asked to measure the size of four objects and their shadows. Please help by making sure that your child's measurements are accurate and recorded correctly. Remind your child that all the shadows should be measured at the same time of day, since the size of a shadow will change as the Sun moves across the sky.

Name:

The Sun in the sky

● Draw a view from your house – perhaps from your bedroom window – in the space below. Keep it simple, but draw the skyline and make sure that you show the sky.

● Several times during one day, draw where the Sun is on your picture. Write the time next to each picture of the Sun.

Remember: do not look directly at the Sun.

You may like to turn your page this way round to draw your picture.

Dear Helper,

Your child may already have completed an activity like this at school. This activity will remind them that the Sun appears to move across the sky in a curve each day. **Please make sure that your child is very careful not to look directly at the Sun during this activity.**

The Sun

● The Sun, the centre of our Solar System, is a truly amazing place. But what can you find out about it? Here are some questions to get you started.

How old is the Sun?

How far away is the Sun?

How hot is the Sun?

What is the Sun's diameter?

Diameter is how far across it is.

● Use the space below to write any interesting 'Sun facts' that you can find. Books, CD-ROMs and the Internet are good places to look for information. Draw pictures to illustrate your work.

Dear Helper,

Encourage your child to look up some basic facts about the Sun. Useful sources of information might include the local library and the Internet. A good starting point on the Internet is http://kids.msfc.nasa.gov. If you are using the Internet, please discourage your child from downloading and printing out lots of information they do not understand. Instead, help them to make notes from which they can write their own account.

The Solar System

● People used to believe that the Earth was at the centre of the Solar System. Imagine this is a newspaper headline breaking the news that actually, it is not. Write the rest of this newspaper report, explaining as much as you can about the Solar System, the Sun and the planets. Draw a picture in the box to illustrate your story.

The Daily Reporter

Earth NOT at centre of Solar System!

_____   _____
_____   _____
_____   _____
_____   _____
_____   _____
_____   _____
_____   _____
_____   _____
_____   _____
_____   _____

Dear Helper,

Please help your child with this task by encouraging them to discuss their ideas, make simple notes and then write their report. Help your child to think of four or five key points, and then to link these together using complete sentences in a brisk, 'newsy' style.

THE SUN AND SHADOWS (EARTH & BEYOND) UNIT 8

Sundials

● We can use a sundial to tell the time from the changing position of the Sun. Use this sheet to make your own sundial.

Instructions

1. Draw a design on the face of your sundial.
2. Cut out the sundial face and the shadow maker (which is called a gnomon).
3. Glue the base of the gnomon onto the dial face as shown.
4. Stand your sundial in a sunny place. At each hour (use a clock to tell you when), mark the time on your sundial.

● Can you put in any hour marks that you missed?

● Can you tell the time using your sundial?

Fold along this line.

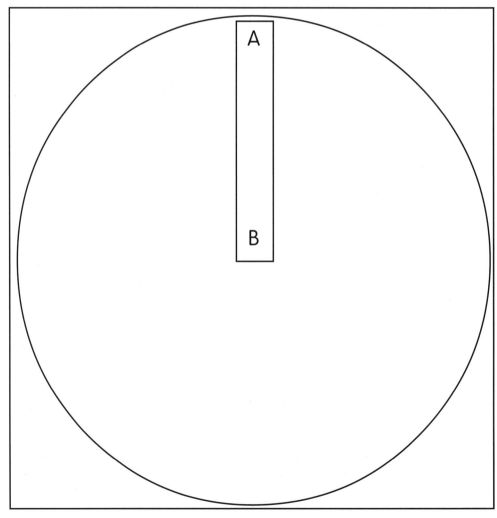

Dear Helper,

Sundials are a traditional method of telling the time. Encourage your child to be creative in their design for a sundial face. This could reflect your child's interests or the landscape where you live. Your child should use the shadow of the gnomon to mark the hours on the dial, so that it can be used for telling the time.

Name:

X-ray observation

You will need: three sheets of rough paper, a pencil.

Have you ever wondered what you look like on the inside? Underneath your skin and layers of muscle and fat are the bones of your skeleton. You can see the shapes of these bones in an X-ray photograph.

If you look closely at your body, you can see some bones under your skin and tell what shape they are even without an X-ray.

● Feel the bones under the skin of your hand. Where are they?

● Clench your fist to see where the knuckles stick out. Draw what you see on a sheet of rough paper.

● Try to make your hand into a stiff claw shape. Where do the bones stick out now? Draw what you see on another sheet.

● Now stretch your hand as wide as you can. Draw what you see on another sheet of rough paper.

● Now you are ready to X-ray! Draw around your hand in the X-ray box above. Use all your bone observations to help you draw what you think the hand's skeleton looks like inside.

Dear Helper,

Your child is investigating the human skeleton. This activity encourages them to observe carefully and record what they see, then use this evidence to draw conclusions about the bone structure of their hand. Encourage them to ask questions, and to record their observations accurately.

PHOTOCOPIABLE

Name:

Growing Gallery

As we grow up, our bodies change in many ways.

● Talk to someone who knew you when you were younger, or someone who can help you decide what you probably looked like.

● Draw pictures and write facts for your own Growing Gallery. If you have any photographs from when you were little, you can use them to help. If you're not sure about the facts, try to make a good guess.

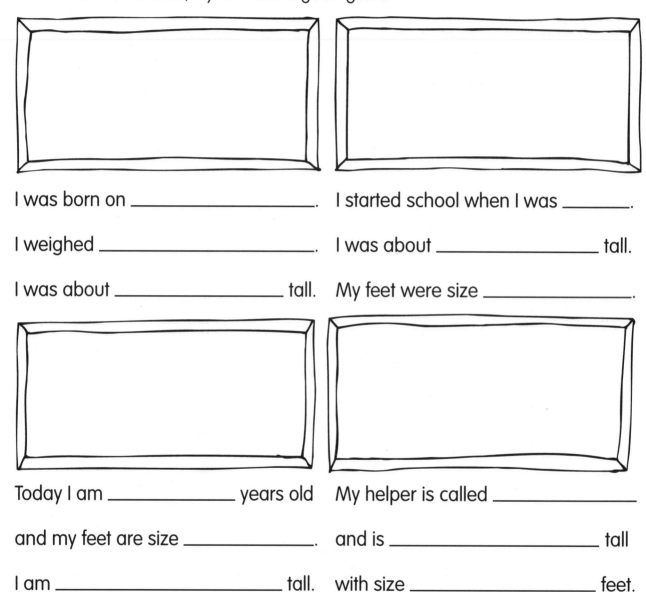

I was born on _____.

I weighed _____.

I was about _____ tall.

I started school when I was _____.

I was about _____ tall.

My feet were size _____.

Today I am _____ years old

and my feet are size _____.

I am _____ tall.

My helper is called _____

and is _____ tall

with size _____ feet.

● How tall was your helper at your age? Compare yourselves now and make a list of the differences you notice on the back of this sheet.

Dear Helper,

Your child is looking at how our skeleton changes as we grow older. They will be asking you questions about their own early years – and yours too! If you have photographs from your child's or your own early years, these will help to give the activity meaning. When you compare yourself and your child, look at the size of hands, feet and head as well as the length of arms and legs.

Name:

Doctor Dreadful's disaster

You will need: scissors and sticky tape.

Doctor Dreadful is having a very bad day!
All the labels have fallen off his body map,
and now he's not sure what's what.
Can you help?

● Draw a line from each label to the right place on the body map.

Body map

lungs

brain

stomach

heart

kidneys

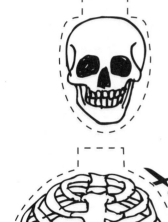

Doctor Dreadful also needs your help to fix some
of the skeleton on the body map. All he knows is that
one piece of the skeleton protects the brain, and
another piece protects the heart and lungs.

● Cut out the two skeleton pieces at the side of the
page. Use the tabs to fix them on the body map
like flaps, so you can still see the bits underneath.

● Write labels for the two pieces of the skeleton on
the body map.

Dear Helper,

Your child has been learning about what is inside them: the main parts of the human body. This activity
will back up what they have done in class and help them to apply this knowledge to their own bodies.

SCHOLASTIC

PHOTOCOPIABLE

79

HOW I MOVE OURSELVES UNIT 1

Top of the hops

When Ravi tried hopping, he used his legs and his feet. He also used his arms to keep his balance.

Afterwards, he decided to record which body parts he had used. He drew axes for a block graph, then drew one square for each body part he had used.

Ravi decided to try more activities and record them on the same graph. He decided to kick a football, eat dinner, read a book, brush his teeth, run for 30 seconds, do a somersault, stretch up high.

● Use your body to do those activities. Record the different parts that you used for each activity on this graph. For some of them, you will be using more than one body part at the same time.

● Write your answers to these questions on the back of this sheet.

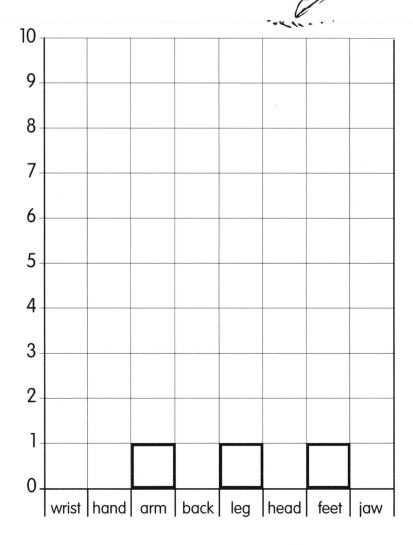

1. Which parts of your body did you use most? Which parts of your body did you only use once?

2. Look at the parts that you only used once. Can you think of some activities that would use them more?

Dear Helper,

Your child has been finding out about the human skeleton. This activity will allow them to show what they have found out, using maths skills to draw a graph. Encourage your child to repeat some of the physical activities in order to check their answers before recording them on the graph.

Name:

Workout

You will need: a tape measure, or some string and a ruler.

● Are you ready to work out? Good! Put some music on if it helps you to move… OK, the first exercise is to flex those arms!

Relax…	**Flex…**	**and relax again!**

● Well done! This time, we're going to measure around the arm muscle when it is relaxed and again when it is flexed. Ready? 1, 2, 3…

My **relaxed** arm muscle measured _____ cm.

My **flexed** arm muscle measured _____ cm.

● OK, now do the same with the thigh muscle. Here we go…

Relax…	**Flex…**	**and relax again!**

My **relaxed** thigh muscle measured _____ cm.

My **flexed** thigh muscle measured _____ cm.

● Try the same exercises with a friend or your helper. Record your results on the back of this sheet, so that you can compare them. How are the measurements for relaxed and flexed muscles different?

Dear Helper,

In class, your child has been finding out about how people move. This activity will help them to discover how our muscles change when we move, and to record these changes using their maths skills. Encourage them to measure carefully and to check their results. If you don't have a tape measure, use string to measure the muscles and then measure the string with a ruler – or your child can bring the string into school to measure with a metre stick.

PHOTOCOPIABLE

Frazzle a friend!

Hi folks, and welcome to the quiz of the week with your host… Johnny Smooth!

This is a quiz with a difference – because you get to ask some of the questions too!

You have three Frazzle chances to help you find the answers! You can **Use A Book**, you can **Try A Computer** or you can **Ask An Adult**. And you can use these three chances as many times as you like! Are you ready?

? How many bones are there in the human skeleton? Circle the answer that is closest to the correct one.

42   714   206   1348

? What do our muscles enable us to do? Circle the correct answer.

grow   hear   move   sleep

The big frazzle!

● Find out a skeleton fact that you can use to ask your friend a question. Write the correct answer on the back of this sheet.

My question: _____

My friend's answer: _____

_____   _____

_____   _____

? In which part of your body would you find your spine? Check your answer by asking an adult or looking at a book or a CD-ROM.

leg   arm   back   heart

● Can you think of any other questions to frazzle your friends? Keep a list of questions to try out in class.

? Humans have a rib cage. Think of three other animals that do. Write their names here, then draw the animals on the back of this sheet.

Human _____

_____   _____

Dear Helper,

Your child has been finding out about the human skeleton in school. This activity gives them an opportunity to do further research. Encourage them to use any sources of information they can find, such as a local library, books at home, CD-ROMs, the Internet or asking people questions. Some children may need help with using computers, reference books and indexes.

📕 SCHOLASTIC

Sort and Snap

You will need: scissors, coloured pencils.

To make a Sort and Snap game, 8 of the squares below

need to have animals on them and the other 8 need plants.

● With your helper, write down as many different animals and plants as you can think of in 5 minutes on a piece of paper. How many were there?

● Choose your favourite 8 plants and 8 animals. Draw and colour them on the empty squares. Make sure you end up with 8 of each!

Ant	_____	_____	Carrot
_____	_____	_____	_____
_____	_____	_____	Tree
_____	Cat	_____	_____

● Cut out the 16 cards, shuffle them and deal them equally between you and your helper. Take turns to play a card. If a card is of the same type as the card before, then shout either **'Plants'** or **'Animals'**. The first player to shout wins the cards that have been played.

● Play until one of you has won all the cards.

● Bring your set of cards to school.

Dear Helper,

Your child has been investigating some of the features of animals and plants. During this activity, encourage your child to think of as many examples as possible. They should think about family pets and their own surroundings, as well as the animals and plants they have seen on holiday or on television. Play several rounds of the game, and encourage your child to increase the number of cards by drawing more pictures on paper and cutting them out.

PHOTOCOPIABLE

Midnight at the House of Doom!

How many different bones and joints do you know?
Skelly Tony knows so many of them that he invited
them around to his house for a midnight party…

Afterwards, to say thank you, all of the guests
wrote Tony a special boney poem.

● Can you write a boney poem about Skelly Tony's party? Think about bones in food, or in your body, or even in a dinosaur skeleton. Use Skelly Tony's guest list below to help you. Can you add some more names to the list?

Jaw   Skull   Elbow   Spine   Ankle

_____   _____   _____

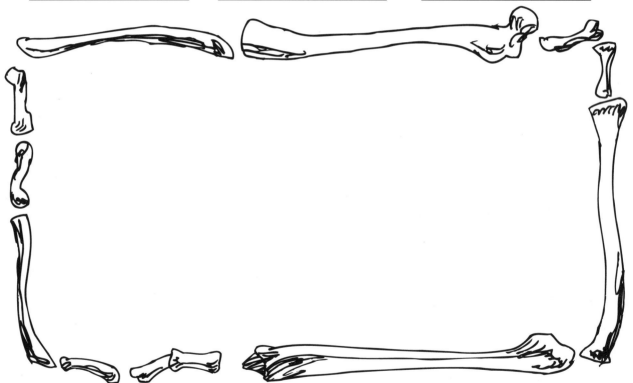

● Write your poem in the bone box above. When you have finished, read your poem out loud. Which bone are you moving when you speak? Circle the right name on the guest list.

Dear Helper,

In class, your child has been finding out about different kinds of animal skeleton and learning the names of some human bones. This activity will encourage them to use these new words along with their creative writing skills. Your child may need help with spellings. Encourage them to think of as many science words as they can for the poem, and remind them that poems don't have to rhyme or be very long!

Sidebar: ANIMALS & PLANTS **UNIT 2** — DIFFERENT SORTS OF SKELETONS — **PHOTOCOPIABLE**

Inside story

X-rays are special photographs that show the bones inside our bodies. Nurse Nabeela was X-raying Curious Craig when the machine broke down! Can you help?

● Complete Craig's X-ray by drawing in the rest of his skeleton.

Craig

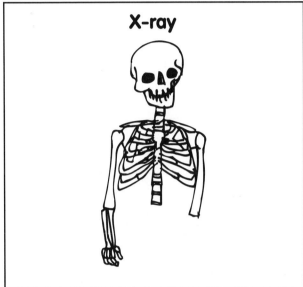

X-ray

● Take a look at the three creatures below. Look at the shapes of their bodies. Think about how they move. What might their skeletons look like?

● Use your ideas to draw X-rays of the three animals for Curious Craig.

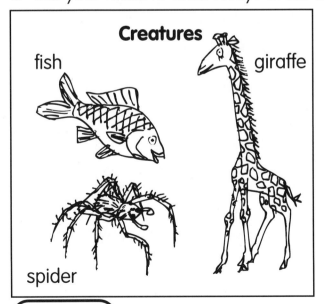

Creatures

fish   giraffe

spider

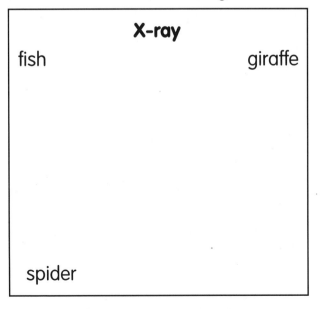

X-ray

fish   giraffe

spider

Dear Helper,

In class, we have been looking at different types of skeleton. Ask your child what they know about this topic. Encourage them to think about the ways that different animals move, and to investigate the differences they notice.

Take care!

You will need: coloured pens or pencils, a blank sheet of paper.

Dozy Dean has been collecting animals for his science project at school. But he is collecting them in the wrong way! It's very dangerous for any animals to be treated like that. Can you help?

● Design a leaflet to help Dean know what to do. You will need to design a cover and research the information.

Cover

Use a bold design to make it clear what the leaflet is about.

You could include a snappy slogan that will grab Dean's attention.

Try out some slogans or titles on your friends and family to see which ones are the best!

Information

What will happen to the living animals we observe if we don't take proper care of them?

What should we do with animals after we have observed them?

You could make a list of dos and don'ts to help Dean.

● Try out some of your ideas on the back of this sheet. When you have decided which is the best way to present your research, you can make the leaflet on a new sheet of paper. Good luck!

Dear Helper,

In class, we have been collecting living creatures and looking at the differences between them. This activity highlights the importance of being careful and responsible when we collect living animals. Encourage your child to get information from any available source, including family members!

Guests at the House of Doom

The House of Doom has many strange guests!

● Look carefully at the pictures below. Use the decision tree to sort out which guest stays in which room. Draw lines to show who goes where. Two of the guests have found their rooms already…

The last owner, Lord Withers, left this message just before he ran away…

I couldn't take it any more! This thing appeared in my study… it was terrible, more than two legs certainly, with a strange tail and a shell that looked harder than iron! It scared me out of my skull!

Who did Lord Withers see? _____

Dear Helper,

Your child has been using 'decision trees' in class to sort living things into groups. This activity will allow them to apply that skill to an unusual situation. Encourage your child to look carefully at the pictures when deciding who (or what) should stay in each guest room.

Name:

Sort it out!

You will need: scissors and glue.

Zoë has an important job at the zoo. Some of the animals have skeletons of bones, but others have skeletons of water or skeletons on the outside. Zoë needs to sort them into the right groups. Can you help?

● Cut out the pictures below. Put animals that have the same kind of skeleton together. When you're sure which groups they belong to, glue them onto the block graph. If you're not sure about an animal, put it in the last column.

● Use the two Bonus Boxes to draw animals of your choice, then add them to the block graph.

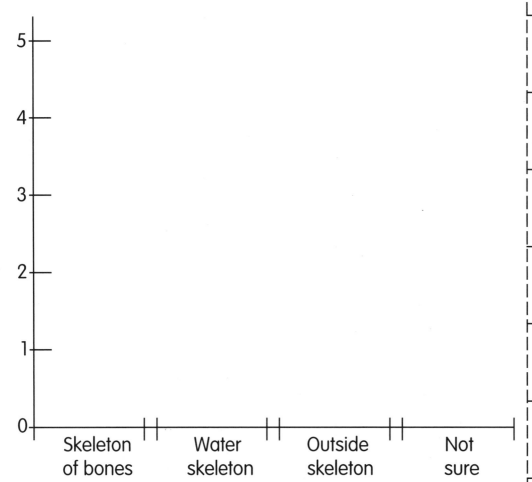

● Which is the most common type of skeleton at Zoë's zoo? Which is the least common type? Write your answers on the back of this sheet.

Dear Helper,

This activity will allow your child to use their knowledge of different skeletons and their graph-drawing skills. Some children may need help with sorting the pictures. Encourage them to use information sources such as books, magazines or the Internet to check their answers.

Name:

My scrapbook

You will need: scissors, glue, magazines, a pen, paper.

Lisa has started collecting pictures for a scrapbook of living things. So far, she has pictures of a tree, a cat and her house.

1. Tree in Lisa's garden

2. Lisa's cat, Scruff

3. Lisa's house

● Before she glues in these pictures, she needs to check that they belong in her scrapbook. She has a chapter for **Living Plants** and one for **Living Animals**. One of her pictures does not belong in either of these chapters. Can you tell her which one it is?

Picture number _____ does **not** belong because _____

_____

● Now you can start to make a scrapbook like Lisa's. Use pictures from old magazines and newspapers to make a collection of living things. Sort them into **Living Plants** and **Living Animals** before gluing them in place.

● Make a title page and a list of contents for your scrapbook. Write an introduction explaining to your readers what your book is about.

| **Dear Helper,** |
| In class, your child has been looking at different types of living things. This activity encourages them to look at the world around them and classify things as living plants, living animals or non-living things (such as cars and houses). Encourage them to look at their own environment and to include pictures of any family pets or drawings of plants from nearby parks and gardens, so that the scrapbook is truly personal to them. |

Name:

Miss Harvey's habitat

You will need: a ruler, a pencil.

Miss Harvey's class are growing bean plants. Bean plants grow best in a warm habitat that is sheltered and has light and water. Miss Harvey and her class planted the beans three weeks ago, and they have grown very quickly!

Debbie's plant is now 26cm tall. 26 is 30 to the nearest 10.

Aaron's plant is 21cm tall. 21 is 20 to the nearest ten.

● Look at the other plants the children have grown (see right).

How tall is Joe's bean plant? _____ cm

Write this height to the nearest 10cm. _____

How tall is Hamna's bean plant?

_____ cm

Write this height to the nearest 10cm.

_____

Add together the heights of all the bean plants.

_____ cm

Write this total to the nearest 10cm.

_____

● Use your answers to draw a bar graph on the back of this sheet. In your graph, show the heights of the children's bean plants rounded to the nearest 10cm.

Dear Helper,

In class, your child has been learning about plants and their habitats. In this homework activity, they can combine their science skills (observing plants) with their maths skills (drawing a graph, a key part of national tests). Encourage your child to round other numbers around them to the nearest 10 – for example, house numbers and prices in shops.

Name:

Ideal Homes Exhibition

Dave is confused. His Ideal Homes Exhibition has six different organisms and six habitats for them to live in. But he has lost his list and doesn't know how to match them up. Can you help?

● Draw a line from each organism to its habitat. One has been done for you.

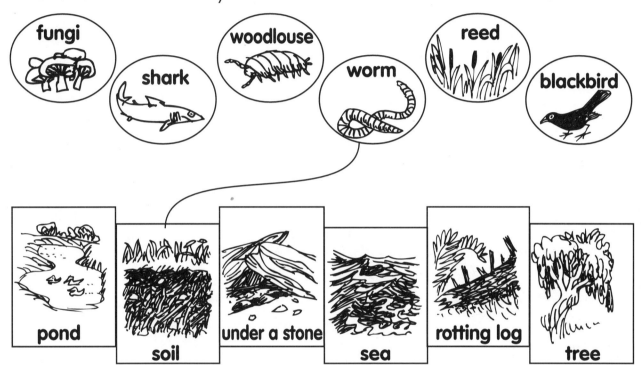

fungi

shark

woodlouse

worm

reed

blackbird

pond

soil

under a stone

sea

rotting log

tree

● Choose one of the organisms and explain why it lives in that habitat. Draw pictures of the organism and its habitat as well.

_____ has_____ as its habitat because

_____

● Dave is a human being. What kind of habitat would suit him?

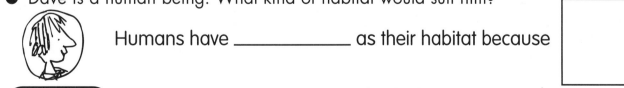

Humans have _____ as their habitat because

_____

Dear Helper,

In class, your child has been studying the places where various plants and animals live (their *habitats*). This activity helps your child to make links between living things and the places where they live. To start with, choose an animal from the list and encourage your child to eliminate the places where it obviously would not live. Encourage them to give reasons as they go along, and to think of examples of places around them.

Name:

What's for dinner?

Professor Fumble's food chain shows
a **producer** and three **consumers**,
but they are all mixed up!
Can you help?

● Cut out the pictures opposite. The **producer** is the plant.
Decide which animal will **consume** it. Which animal is
next in the food chain? Which comes last? Stick the
pictures on the back of this sheet, with arrows to show
the order of the food chain. Label each picture as
producer or **consumer**.

Professor Fumble is a consumer. Tonight, she is going to
eat a beef steak – her favourite!

● Only three of the pictures below are part of this food
chain. Find the right pictures and number them to show
the order they come in. On the back of this sheet write a
description of the food chain, explaining which living
thing is the **producer** and which are the **consumers**.

fly

vole

plant

fox

grass

Professor Fumble

fox

horse

● What are you having for dinner tonight?
Choose one part of your meal and write
a food chain for it. Label the **producer**
and the **consumers** in this food chain.

cow

Dear Helper,

In class, your child has been looking at how different animals eat different things, and how they are linked
up by *food chains* in which larger animals eat smaller animals. In this activity, your child can make links
between animals and plants, and see how humans fit into food chains. Encourage them to think about how
food gets to their plates, and to read the lists of ingredients on food cans or packets.

Name:

What's cooking?

You will need: coloured pencils.

Katie loves a fry up! Today she is cooking sausages, chips, beans, mushrooms, bacon, eggs and black pudding.

Animals that eat only meat are called **carnivores**.

Those that eat only vegetables are called **herbivores**.

● Decide with your helper which foods on Katie's plate could be eaten by a carnivore and which by a herbivore. Colour them using this code: red for meat and green for vegetables.

● Katie cooked one thing that is neither meat nor a vegetable. What is it? Does it come from an animal or a plant?

_____

● What do you like to eat? You and your helper can each write a menu showing your favourite foods, then swap them and underline all the meats in red and the vegetables in green. Are any of the foods neither meat nor vegetables?

Human beings are naturally **omnivores**. This means they can eat both meat and vegetables. Some people do not eat certain foods for religious, cultural or medical reasons.

● Talk about this with your helper. Write down a list of facts that you know and things you would like to find out on the back of this sheet.

Dear Helper,

In class, your child has been learning about the different foods that animals eat. This activity will encourage them to look at their own foods at home and think about the different types of food they may eat. Be prepared to discuss your own choice of food with them!

Name:

Dinner for two?

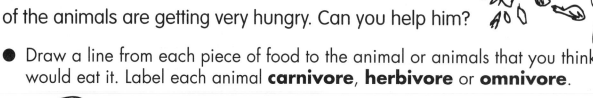

You will need: blue and green pens.

Clumsy Chris has muddled all the food at the zoo!

All the meat and vegetables are mixed up, and some

of the animals are getting very hungry. Can you help him?

● Draw a line from each piece of food to the animal or animals that you think would eat it. Label each animal **carnivore**, **herbivore** or **omnivore**.

chimpanzee

grass

beans

crocodile

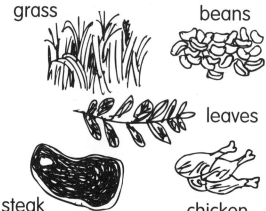

lion

leaves

steak

chicken

antelope

Humans often eat different foods from each other.

Hi, I'm Sam and I am vegetarian. Draw a green line under the foods I would eat from Chris's menu.

CHRIS'S MENU
Tomato soup
Prawn cocktail
Burger and chips
Cheesy baked potato
Ham salad
Broccoli and Stilton quiche
Toffee ice cream

Hi. I'm Rosa and I am omnivorous. Draw a blue ring around the foods I would eat from Chris's menu.

● How many of the foods have both a green line and a blue ring?

Dear Helper,

In class, your child has been learning about the different foods that are eaten by different animals. This activity encourages them to compare different diets and think about different types of food. Please discuss what foods your child likes and dislikes, and whether these are meat or vegetable foods.

Name:

Disappearing aliens

You will need: coloured pencils, scissors, glue.

Zip and Zap are aliens. In the picture below, they have used a colour disappearing ray to make themselves harder to see. Can you find them?

● Colour in the picture, using the colour key to help you. Colour each part that is marked 1 green, each part that is marked 2 yellow, and so on.

Colour key

1 = green

2 = yellow

3 = blue

4 = orange

5 = brown

6 = black

7 = red

8 = grey

Can you see the aliens more clearly now?

● Cut out Zip and Zap and stick them in the box below. Can you design a habitat that will give them better camouflage?

Dear Helper,

In class, your child has been looking at different animals and where they live. Many creatures have a colour and shape that help them to blend into their backgrounds or *habitats*. This blending is called *camouflage*. Encourage your child to colour in the picture carefully, using the colour key. When your child is designing a habitat that will camouflage Zip and Zap, encourage them to think about what colours they need to use and what kind of background has those colours.

PHOTOCOPIABLE

Park life

You will need: coloured pencils.

Sarah looks after the plants and animals in the park. She sees a lot of changes as the seasons turn from hot summer to cooler autumn to cold winter to warmer spring and then back to summer again.

● Colour in the first picture. In the summer the trees have green leaves and the flowers bloom. Humans use the paddling pool, eat ice creams and sit in the shade. The baby ducks have grown and hedgehogs are sometimes seen walking under the bushes.

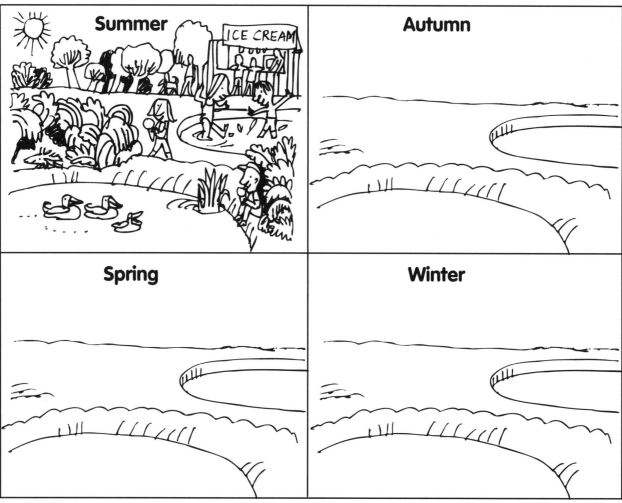

● Can you finish off drawing and colouring the pictures for autumn, winter and spring? Make sure you include the ducks, hedgehog, humans and trees.

Dear Helper,

In class, your child has been finding out about how the seasons affect animals and plants. This activity helps them to make links between these effects and their own behaviour. Talk to them about their summer holidays: what do they eat, do and wear? How does this compare with the winter? To help them make personal links, you could also talk about the changes to a family pet (such as moulting) and the changes to plants in the garden or a local park.

Material world

Inspector Nosey, ace detective, at your service.

Today I am investigating… materials. You're surrounded

by them, even in your own home! Help me track them down…

● In your home, there are many things made from glass, metal and cloth. Choose one of each type of material and fill in the details below.

Investigation file: **glass**

This is a _____

It feels _____

It is used for _____

Draw it here.

Investigation file: **metal**

This is a _____

It feels _____

It is used for _____

Investigation file: **cloth**

This is a _____

It feels _____

It is used for _____

● And it doesn't stop there, oh no! How many other things are there in your home made from the same materials? Write a list of them on the back of this sheet. Open up your own investigation files on plastic and wood. See, what did I tell you? We're surrounded by materials!

Dear Helper,

In class, your child has been looking at different materials and their uses in everyday life. This activity encourages them to look at some familiar things at home, and to think about what materials they are made from and why. Encourage them to look closely. Please discuss why certain materials are not used for certain purposes – for example, why a chocolate teapot would be useless.

PHOTOCOPIABLE

■ SCHOLASTIC

MATERIALS **UNIT 4**

WARM LIQUIDS, COOL SOLIDS

Where in the world?

Class 4 have been on their holidays. They sent back postcards from the places they went to. They found out the temperature by looking at a thermometer. The temperature tells us how hot or cold a place is.

● Read the first three thermometers below and fill in the missing temperatures.

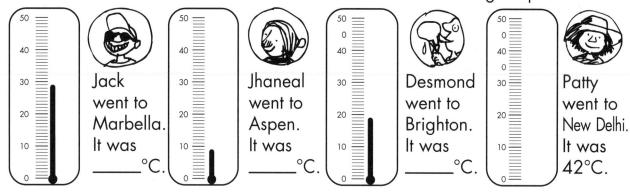

Jack went to Marbella. It was _____°C.

Jhaneal went to Aspen. It was _____°C.

Desmond went to Brighton. It was _____°C.

Patty went to New Delhi. It was 42°C.

● Can you draw the temperature in New Delhi on Patty's thermometer for her?

● Now try Class 4's quiz. Show your answers and working out in the box below.

1. Add the temperatures that Jack and Patty measured. What do you get?

2. Who was colder, Jhaneal or Desmond?

3. How many degrees warmer was Patty than Desmond?

4. How many degrees colder was Desmond than Jack?

● Make up your own question to add to Class 4's quiz. Can your helper answer it?

Dear Helper,

Your child has been learning in class about temperatures and how to use a thermometer. This activity will help them link using a thermometer to basic addition and subtraction skills. Encourage them to write down their working out, and don't be surprised if their jottings don't look like your way of writing out such sums!

Blake's temperature trauma

Hey folks, Blake Midwinter here with this week's 'World of Weather'… HEY! WHAT'S HAPPENED TO MY SCRIPT?

● Someone has forgotten to fill in the temperatures on Blake's weather script. All the information he needs is in the bar graph below. Can you help to fill the gaps in his script?

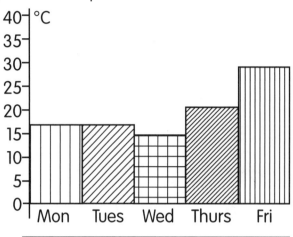

Weather script

Well, as you can see, it's been pretty chilly here lately. The top temperature for Thursday was just _____ – although it got warmer on Friday, reaching up to _____. The coldest day of the week was _____ , with a temperature of _____. Monday and Tuesday were both below _____ degrees.

That's all for now, folks. I'm Blake Midwinter and you've been watching 'World of Weather'.

● Now try to record the temperature of the place where you live for the next five days. You can get this information from radio, TV, local newspapers or the Internet.

● Use your data to draw a graph underneath Blake's.

Hey, thanks for helping out! Now write a weather script for the place where you live! Write it on the back of this sheet.

Dear Helper,

In class, your child has been looking at temperatures and comparing hot and cold things. This activity helps them to apply what they have learned to their own environment, and to use science ideas in an everyday situation. Encourage your child to use more than one of the information sources suggested.

Name:

The revenge of Doctor Chill

Zip and Zap are space explorers. Their mission is to rescue Prince Vince from the evil Doctor Chill…

● Can you help? Look at the contents of Zap's survival kit. Draw a circle around each thing that might help them to get the key.

● Finish the story in the space below! Use the same style as above. Show how Zip and Zap used things from the survival kit to get the key out of the ice block. Use the back of this sheet if you need more space.

Dear Helper,

In class, your child has seen the effects of heat and cold on different materials. This activity leads them to apply this knowledge to an unusual situation. A good way to start would be to discuss what is needed to free the key from the ice block. Then look at how some items in the survival kit could be used together, but others could not be used. You could try out your child's ideas with an ice cube from the freezer.

At home with Zip and Zap

Zip and Zap's space station is on the planet Yuggoth. For a temporary home on a cold planet, it's quite comfortable.

● Look at the space station. Find ten things in it that are solid, and put a red tick next to each one. Now look carefully for liquids. Put a blue circle around each liquid that you can see.

● Draw a room from your own home in the box below. Put a blue tick next to ten solids in your drawing, and draw a red circle around any liquids. Make a list of the solids and liquids on the back of this sheet.

Jelly journal

Safety! You must ask your helper to pour the boiling water.

You will need: a pencil, a packet of jelly cubes, a bowl, a plate, a clock or watch, a kettle, a helper.

● Take the jelly out of the packet. Feel it.

● Is it solid or liquid? _____

● Follow the instructions on the packet. Ask your helper to pour the boiling water onto the jelly cubes. Wait for 5 minutes.

● Is it solid or liquid? _____

● Now let the mixture cool for 20 minutes. Time it with your helper, then put the mixture into the fridge for 1 hour.

● What do you think will happen to the mixture while it is in the fridge?

I predict that _____

My helper predicts that _____

● Take the mixture out of the fridge. Turn it out of the bowl onto a plate.

● Is it solid or liquid? _____

● What effects did the coldness of the fridge have on the mixture? Talk about it, then write an answer you both agree with on the back of this sheet.

Draw the jelly cubes here.

Draw the jelly in boiling water here.

Draw what the jelly looks like now.

Dear Helper,

In class, your child has been looking at solids and liquids. This activity helps your child to look at an everyday situation in which a solid changes to a liquid, which then changes back into a solid. The key skills your child will develop here are predicting, observing and timing. Encourage them to share their ideas about what is happening with you. Can they explain why you made your own prediction? Afterwards, you can enjoy the jelly for tea!

Light me!

This is a drawing of an electric circuit. The different parts or components are labelled. When the circuit is switched on, the bulb will light.

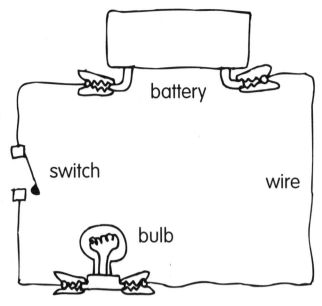

● Is it switched on now?

Yes ☐   No ☐

● Look at these circuits.

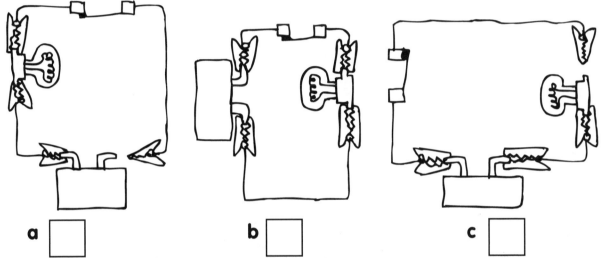

a ☐   b ☐   c ☐

● Tick the circuit that will light the bulb.

● Explain why this circuit will light the bulb. _____

_____

● Choose one circuit that will not light the bulb and explain why. _____

_____

● Choose one circuit that will not light the bulb. Can you fix it? On the back of this sheet, draw and label your new circuit and explain how you made it work.

Name:

Batteries or mains?

 Be safe! Never touch plugs or sockets.

● How many **appliances** in your home need electricity to make them work? Have a look around your house and write a list of them on the back of this sheet. Large appliances, such as TV sets, are powered by electricity from the **mains** circuit. They have plugs to connect them to the mains power supply. Mains electricity is very powerful and can be dangerous.

● How many of your appliances have plugs? Put a tick for each one in the top row of this chart. Add them up.

		Total
Appliances with plugs		
Appliances with batteries		

Smaller appliances, such as torches, can be powered by electricity from battery circuits. These appliances don't need plugs. Batteries are less powerful than the mains.

● How many of your appliances have batteries? Put a tick for each one in the bottom row of the chart above. Add them up.

● Now use the data you have collected to draw this bar graph.

● Everyone needs to know the dangers of mains electricity. Can you think of a good slogan that will remind people of the dangers?

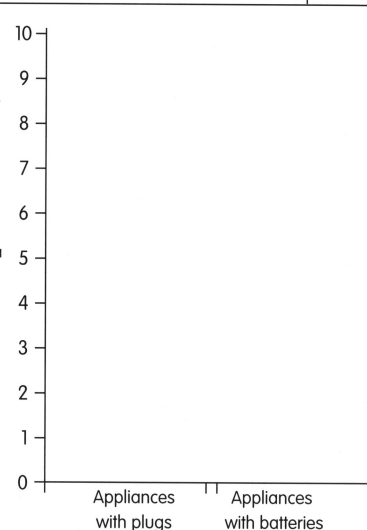

Dear Helper,

In class, your child has been learning about how we use electricity safely. As part of this work, they have looked at different sources of electrical power. Encourage them to find as many different examples of mains and battery-operated appliances in the home as possible. **Remind your child not to touch plugs or sockets, and emphasise why: electric shocks from the mains can be fatal! Explain that batteries can be dangerous too, and should never be opened.**

Delivery day

Poor Barney Bright has a big delivery of electrical appliances at his shop... and his assistant is off sick! The new stock needs to be sorted into groups. Can you help?

Each appliance uses electricity to heat things up, cool things down, produce light or make something move.

● Draw a line from each appliance to the right label for what it does.

Heat _____   _____ **Cool**

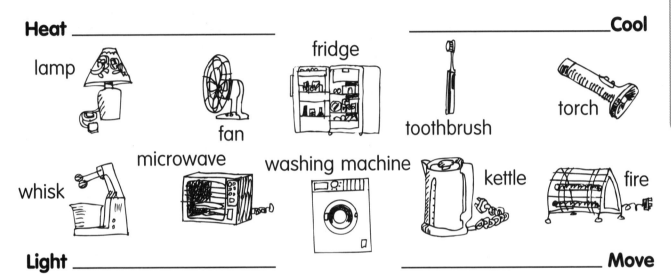

lamp   fan   fridge   toothbrush   torch

whisk   microwave   washing machine   kettle   fire

Light _____   _____ **Move**

● In the spaces above, write the name of one more electrical appliance in each group.

With all this extra work to do, Barney has not had time to add up his stock. Can you help?

● He needs to know how many appliances he has in each group, and how many he has altogether. Show all your working out and write your answers on the right.

BRIGHT'S
electricals

Dear Helper,

In class, your child has been finding out about sources of electricity and the different uses that electricity can be put to. This activity links our class work to your home setting. Encourage your child to look at different electrical appliances at home and discuss what you use them for.

⚠ **Remind your child not to touch any plugs or cables!**

The Insulation Station

You will need: paper and coloured pencils.

Zip and Zap are escaping from the dastardly Luke Leccy's Insulation Station…

- No wonder they can't see – Luke Leccy has replaced some parts of this circuit with insulators! Can you spot them? Draw a circle around each insulator.

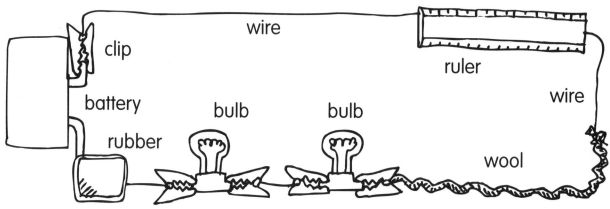

- Quick, take a look in Zap's survival pack! Are there any things they could use to repair the circuit? Draw a circle around each conductor.

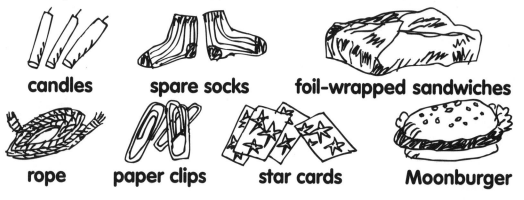

- On the back of this sheet, finish off the story with words and pictures. Make sure you explain why Zip and Zap should use certain things from the survival pack and not others if they are going to escape!

Dear Helper,

In class, your child has been learning that some materials conduct electricity and others do not. Materials that do not conduct electricity are called *insulators*. This activity encourages them to think about which materials are conductors and which are insulators. Encourage your child to say what all the things in Zap's pack are likely to be made of.

Circus circuits

You will need: scissors, glue, a pencil.

Moriarty's circus has come to town!
He has made a big poster that will
light up for everyone to see.

At the moment he has one bulb,
one battery and a switch in his circuit.
It doesn't look very bright! Can you help?

● Cut out all the circuit components. With your helper,
design a circuit that will light up the poster brightly.
Glue the components around the poster and draw
the connecting wires to complete your circuit.

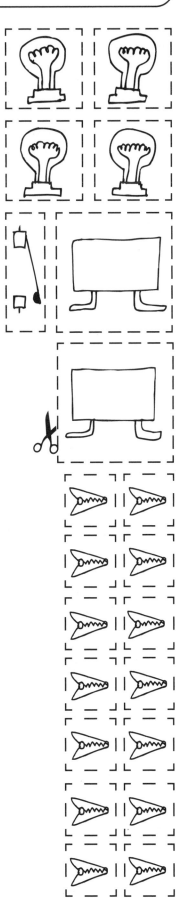

PHOTOCOPIABLE

Name:

Stand back, Zip and Zap!

Zip and Zap are aliens visiting Earth. They don't know how to use electrical things, and sometimes they do things that are dangerous!

Zip is trying to listen to a CD. But he can't hear anything!

● Explain what he should do.

_____

Zap is going to dry her hair. Her hands are still wet from the shower. **STOP, ZAP!**

● What should she do to be safe?

_____

Zip and Zap have bought lots of electrical items and plugged them all in together.

● Is this safe? Explain your answer.

_____

_____

● Zip and Zap need help! Write a leaflet on the back of this sheet to teach them how to use electricity properly. Use these headings to help you. Tick them off as you use each one.

Title and introduction		Circuits and switches		Insulators and conductors	
Plugs and batteries		Using electricity safely!		Electricity at home	

Dear Helper,

In class, your child has been learning about the ways we use electricity and the safety rules we need to follow. This activity helps them to collect together all the things they have learned. If you have information leaflets on any subject (for example, health leaflets), encourage your child to read them and think about how they present facts and instructions.

Name:

Push, pull or twist dominoes

You will need: coloured pencils, glue, scissors, cardboard (such as old birthday cards).

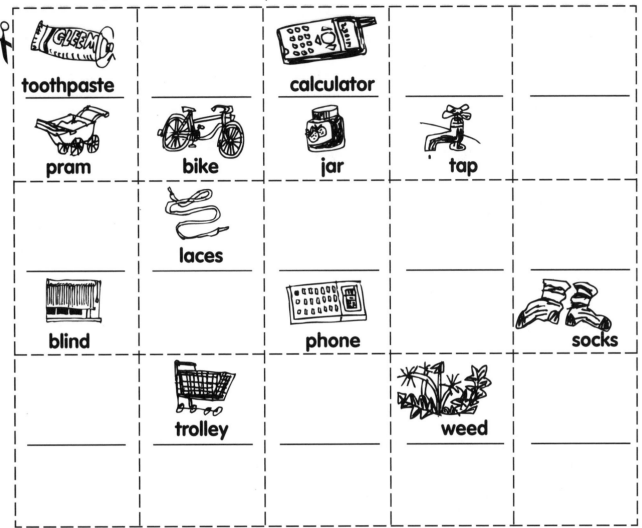

toothpaste		calculator		
pram	bike	jar	tap	
	laces			
blind		phone		socks
	trolley		weed	

This is a game of dominoes with a twist! Instead of dots, each domino has pictures of things that you push, pull or twist.

● Draw an arrow to show the direction of the push, pull or twist in each drawing. The first arrow has been drawn for you.

● With your helper, make a list of other things that you can push, pull or twist. Draw them in the blank spaces on the dominoes.

● Cut out the dominoes and glue them onto cardboard. Play a game of dominoes by matching things that will push, pull or twist. Who will win?

Dear Helper,

In class, your child has been finding out about different kinds of forces. In this activity, they will find examples of things at home that are pushed, pulled and twisted. The dominoes game involves deciding which force is used each time. Encourage your child to come up with an equal number of *push*, *pull* and *twist* objects for the blank spaces. Add extra dominoes if your child has more ideas. Enjoy the game!

PHOTOCOPIABLE

Name:

Siân's speedy skittles 1

You will need: a crayon (the waxy type is best).

Siân loves ten-pin bowling. In fact, she's so keen that she has decided to make her own bowling alley at home so she can practise.

Siân has collected some empty plastic fizzy drinks bottles and a tennis ball to play with. Now she needs to decide which surface to use. She's not sure whether to use brick, concrete or tiles. Can you help?

● Read the Friction Factfile. Can you predict which surface will be best for bowling? Write it on the back of this sheet.

● Try brick first. Make a crayon rubbing of a brick surface in the rectangle on the right. Think about how bumpy or smooth it feels.

● Do a rubbing of a concrete surface in the oval. Was it smoother or bumpier than the brick?

● Do a rubbing of a tiled surface in the triangle. Was there more or less friction than with the other surfaces?

● From the results of your investigation, decide which surface Siân should choose for her bowling alley. Write down your answer and explain it on the back of this sheet.

● Compare your answer with your prediction. Are they the same?

Friction Factfile

The less **friction** there is between a ball and a surface, the faster the ball will travel.

When you make a rubbing of a surface, you will feel **friction** through the paper. The bumpier it feels, the more **friction** there is.

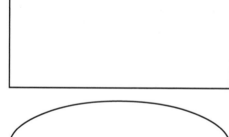

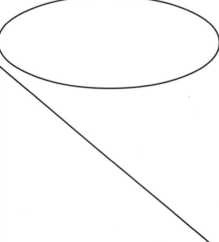

Dear Helper,

In class, your child has been learning about friction. This activity encourages them to carry out a practical investigation and explain the results. Help your child to find brick, concrete and tiled surfaces in or around the home. Encourage them to think their ideas through, and to explain their prediction and their final answer to you.

SCHOLASTIC

100 SCIENCE HOMEWORK ACTIVITIES ● YEAR 4

Friction Rollerball

You will need: a cardboard tube or rolled-up sheet of paper, a marble or small ball, a ruler or tape measure, a pencil.

Ruth and Freya were trying to see to see who could roll a ball furthest. They used a box that was 20cm high. Then they leant a tube against it so that the bottom of the tube was 60cm away from the box.

Then they each chose two different test surfaces. They set the box and tube up the same way each time, so it was a fair test. They rolled the ball from the top of the tube and measured how far it travelled along the test surface. Here are their results:

Ruth	Surface 1: Carpet = 8cm	Surface 2: Tiles = 29cm
Freya	Surface 3: Concrete = 23cm	Surface 4: Grass = 4cm

● Write **true** next to each sentence you agree with.

Distance the ball travelled on carpet > distance it travelled on grass.

Friction between ball and concrete < friction between ball and tiles.

Freya's distances added together > Ruth's distances added together.

● Now try Friction Rollerball for yourself. Choose your test surfaces and set up the game just as Ruth and Freya did. Record your results in the table below.

Surface 1:	=	**cm**	Surface 2:	=	**cm**
Surface 3:	=	**cm**	Surface 4:	=	**cm**

● Use your results to decide which of these sentences are true.

Distance the ball travelled on surface 1 > distance on surface 3.

Friction between the ball and surface 2 < friction with surface 4.

Distance the ball travelled on surface 4 < distance on surface 1.

Dear Helper,

In class, your child has been learning about friction and the effect it has on how far an object can travel. In this activity, they have to use maths skills and science knowledge to present their results and decide which of the sentences are true. Encourage them to think of new sentences using the < and > signs to test their friends.

Name:

Force report

Rukeya is a reporter for the *Daily Force*. It is her job to report things that happen and explain what forces were involved. Last week, she had to report a big story involving **friction**…

Mad Mark's near miss!

At six o'clock last Thursday, residents of Sleepytown Road were shocked to witness what could have been a very nasty accident.

Friction is the force made when two different surfaces rub together. The tread marks on car tyres cause friction between the tyres and the surface of the road. A car's brakes use friction to stop the wheels going round. Mark's car skidded because the brakes suddenly reduced the wheels' grip on the road.

Mad Mark, well known for driving his silver sports car at high speeds, was just about to turn the corner. The tyres had a good grip on the road, since they were new and had deep tread marks.

All seemed fine. Then suddenly, a little puppy named Lucky ran onto the street. A shocked Mad Mark said: "I saw Lucky and swerved so I wouldn't hit him. I slammed on my brakes and skidded before I stopped. It was pretty scary actually…"

Lucky has been returned to his home. Mad Mark has bought a bicycle. Friction saved the day!

This week, Rukeya is going to report a story about **gravity**. This is what happened…

Precious   Rhys

● Rukeyah's lost her notes! Can you write the report for her? Set it out like the one about Mad Mark. You need to include: a **headline**, an **introduction**, the **story**, a **force explanation** and an **ending**. Draft out your report on another sheet of paper, then use the back of this sheet for your final report.

Dear Helper,

In class, your child has been learning how to write a report in an ordered way. In this activity, they will apply this writing skill to science, using ideas they know from class work. Encourage your child to compare this report with ones in a newspaper. What features are the same? What features are different?

Name:

A game of two forces

You will need: two straws, a ping-pong ball (or screwed-up piece of paper), pipe cleaners and Plasticine (or card strips and sticky tape), a table.

Sam and Mags are playing a blow football cup final.

Mags is winning 2–1, but Sam has a penalty…

He takes a deep breath…   He blows down his straw…   GOAL!

● Look at the pictures above with your helper. Draw an arrow on the middle picture to show the direction of the force Sam is using to score his goal.

When Mags scored the first goal, this is what happened…

Mags blew down her straw. The ball moved. When Sam blew down his straw, the ball slowed down. When Sam stopped blowing, Mags scored!

● Draw arrows to show the directions of the forces. Discuss them with your helper. Why did the ball slow down? Why did it move quickly again?

● Set up a game of blow football. Try blowing the ball at the same time as your helper. What happens when one of you stops? Why is this? Record your ideas on the back of this sheet.

● Play your own Cup Final. Use pipe cleaners to make goalposts, and fix them to opposite ends of a table with Plasticine (or use card strips and sticky tape). Each half of the game is 5 minutes long, and you can't touch the ball.

Dear Helper,   **My team**   v   **My helper's team**

In class, your child has been finding out about forces in everyday life. This activity will help your child to identify the directions of pushing forces and show them on a diagram. Encourage your child to think about how strong these forces are. Play several rounds of blow football for a knockout championship!

Siân's speedy skittles 2

You will need: five fizzy drinks cans, a tennis ball, graph paper, a pencil, a ruler, a tape measure.

Siân is holding a bowling championship, using cans as skittles. She bowls the ball along a surface, causing **friction**. When the ball hits a skittle, the **impact** causes more **friction** and some skittles are knocked over. **Gravity** pulls them down.

Siân stands 3m away from the skittles each time she bowls. She has 3 bowls. She sets up all the skittles before each bowl, and scores 1.5 points for each skittle she knocks over.

Player	First bowl	Second bowl	Third bowl
Siân	4.5 points	1.5 points	7.5 points
You			

How many skittles did Siân knock over with her third bowl? _____

● Now it's your turn! Set up your cans like Siân's and stand 3 metres away. Mark the place with a line, so you can always stand the same distance away. How well can you do? Write your results in the table above, remembering the points scale: 1 skittle = 1.5 points.

● Now draw a bar chart on graph paper to show how many **points** you and Siân scored each time you bowled. Remember to draw and label the axes.

● Answer these questions on your graph paper.

1. Which is the smallest bar on the bar chart?

2. Look at the tallest bar. How many points does it represent?

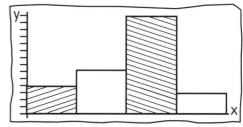

3. Look at the bar for your third bowl. How many skittles does it represent?

● If you filled the cans with water, what effect do you think this would have on your bowling score? Write a prediction to test at school.

Dear Helper,

In class, your child has been investigating forces. This activity involves playing a game, then presenting and discussing the results, using the same skills that your child would use to carry out an investigation and draw conclusions from the results. Encourage your child to play several rounds of the game in order to increase their bowling accuracy!

Name:

Disappearing tricks

Wizard Worrybuttle has cast a spell! He's made Professor Fumble's science words disappear from her report into a wordsearch. Can you help him make them appear again?

● Some of the words are written forwards in the wordsearch, but others are written vertically or even backwards! When you find a word, draw a ring around it and write it in the right place in Professor Fumble's report. Wizard Worrybuttle has managed to find one, but now he's stuck…

1. Scientists draw an _____**arrow**_____ to show the direction of a force.

2. When two surfaces rub together, the force is called _____.

3. _____ is the name of the force that pulls things down.

4. _____ will pull certain metal items towards them.

5. The units we use to measure force are called _____.

6. Paper spinners can be used to measure _____ resistance.

7. The information we learn from an experiment is called a _____.

● There is one more science word hidden in the wordsearch. Can you find it and write a sentence explaining what it means? Clue: it is written backwards!

N	E	F	R	I	C	T	I	O	N
E	R	G	A	P	S	O	M	E	T
W	A	R	R	O	W	M	A	R	I
T	O	A	N	E	L	P	G	U	B
O	M	V	U	O	A	Y	N	L	O
N	O	I	T	C	I	D	E	R	P
S	U	T	H	E	R	E	T	O	M
M	L	Y	L	T	L	U	S	E	R

Dear Helper,

In class, your child has been finding out about forces and how they influence our everyday lives. This activity tests your child's knowledge of the scientific vocabulary used when we talk about forces. Encourage them to explain the meaning of each word to you. They could use a dictionary to check the words and the meanings.

Shadow Theatre presents:
Trapped in the House of Doom!

You will need: glue, a cereal box, a torch, tissue paper or thin cloth, straws, old cards.

● Trace the outline of these characters onto card and cut them out.

Matt   **Vikki**   **Professor Fang**   **Lady Cobweb**

● Stick a straw onto the back of each figure.

● These are your shadow puppets. Now set up your shadow theatre like this…

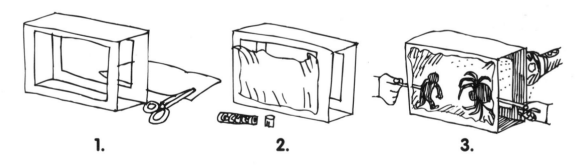

1.   **2.**   **3.**

1. Cut a rectangle out of the front and back of your cereal box.

2. Glue tissue paper over the front. Shine the torch from the back.

3. Your characters can use the entrance at the side!

● Put Professor Fang in the middle of the stage and shine the torch. With your helper, take turns to look at the stage from the front. Move the characters around on the stage to see what the shadows look like. Decide who will play teach character – there are two each.

● Here is the start of your script. The stage directions (written in brackets) tell you what to do. Use your puppets to act out the script.

In the entrance hall of the House of Doom…

Matt: (*shaking*) I don't like the look of this place Vikki, it's too spooky!

Vikki: Don't be such a scaredy cat! It's a bit mucky, that's all. Anyway, the man in the village said there would be room here and we can leave when the storm is over… (*Turn the torchlight off and on quickly three times.*)

Matt: Yikes! What was **that**?

Vikki: Just lightning! Come on, let's find the owner and ask if we can stay. (*Professor Fang flies in.*)

Prof. Fang: May I be of assistance…Master Matt and Mistress Vikki?

Vikki: Oh, er, yes, yes please. We need –

Matt: He knew our names already. Double spooky! That's it, I'm off.

Prof. Fang: I think not, my friends. Besides, I've sealed the doors… haven't I, Lady Cobweb? (*Lady Cobweb comes down from the ceiling.*)

Matt and Vikki: (*both jump up in the air*)

AAAAAAARRRRRRRRGGGGGGGGHHHHHH!

Unfortunately, the writer got too scared to finish the play! Can you help?

● Continue the script on the back of this sheet. You can add new characters and scenery if you like. Don't forget to include stage directions.

● Which shapes make the clearest shadows? What happens to the shadows when the torch is further away? Write your answers on the back of this sheet.

Dear Helper,

In class, your child has been learning about light and shadows. This activity helps them to look closely at shadows and how they are made while creating a fun (and slightly scary) shadow play. Encourage your child to try different angles of lighting and different puppets, and to decide which combinations are best for creating bold, clear shadows. Can they explain why this happens?

How light travels

You will need: a cardboard tube, black paper, greaseproof paper, sticky tape or elastic bands, a pin.

Superstriker Shane is about to take a very important penalty. He looks at the goalkeeper... but how does he see him?

When light reflects off an object, it enters the front of the eye and forms an image at the back of the eye. If there is no light to reflect off an object, then you can't see it!

Shane scores the goal! He decides to find out more by making a pinhole camera. A pinhole camera works in a similar way to an eye: the light travels in a straight line to the back of it. Can you help?

- Cut some greaseproof paper so that it fits over one end of a cardboard tube with some left over. Make sure it is pulled tight, and fix it with sticky tape or an elastic band.

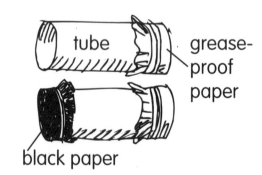

tube   grease-proof paper

black paper

- Do the same with black paper at the other end of the tube. Make sure that there are no gaps, as they will let extra light in and spoil your results.

- Use the pin to make a tiny single pinhole in the middle of the black paper. Now point your tube at a brightly lit object, the pinhole end first. What do you see on the greaseproof paper?

- On the back of this sheet, draw the image that was reflected onto your greaseproof paper. What do you notice about the image? You could use a library book, a CD-ROM or the Internet to find out why this is.

Dear Helper,

In class, your child has been finding out about light and how it travels. This activity will help them to understand the way they see things around them. Help your child to make the pinhole camera. Encourage them to observe the image in the 'camera' carefully, and to find out (by reading) why this image is produced. A trip to the library might be helpful for this.

Name: _____

Wake up, Grandma!

Every day, when Sahid got home from school, his Grandma was asleep in front of the TV! He decided to try some different ways of waking her up…

He shook the shaker on Monday, crashed the cymbals on Tuesday, beat the drum on Wednesday, blew the whistle on Thursday and rang the bell on Friday!

Grandma always woke up – but he had to shake, crash, beat, blow or ring some instruments more than others! He recorded his results in a pictogram.

Scale: 1 [icon] = 2 shakes, crashes, beats, whistles or rings

		Number
Monday: shaker	[7 icons]	
Tuesday: cymbals	[1 icon]	
Wednesday: drum	[1 icon]	
Thursday: whistle	[2 icons]	
Friday: bell		7

● Sahid rang the bell 7 times before Grandma woke up. Can you draw the last row of the pictogram for him?

● Can you fill in the rest of the numbers for Sahid? Remember the scale.

● Now use the pictogram to help you answer these questions.

1. Which instrument did Sahid use 4 times? _____

2. How many times did Sahid bang the drum? _____

3. Which instrument did he use more times, the whistle or the bell? _____

4. Which instrument took the longest time to wake Grandma? _____

5. Which instrument woke Grandma up most quickly? _____

Dear Helper,

In class, your child has been learning about different methods of recording scientific data. These skills are important for success in national tests. In this activity, they have to apply their data handling skills in order to answer questions about the effects of different sounds. Remind them not to try this experiment at home!

Which pitch?

You will need: a ruler, a pencil.

James and Patty are testing the different pitches of sound they can make…

● To join in, just place your ruler so it reaches 10cm over the edge of the table, hold it down with one hand… and twang it! Describe the sound it makes.

● Now hold the ruler so it reaches 20cm over the edge of the table. Before you twang it again, make a **pitch prediction**. Patty predicts the pitch will be higher, James predicts it will be lower. What do you predict? Tick one box.

Higher ☐   Lower ☐   The same ☐

● Twang the ruler. Was the result what you predicted?

● Try twanging the ruler at different lengths. Compare the pitch of the sounds.

● Only one of these statements is true. Use what you have found out to decide which one it is. Mark each box T (true) or F (false).

When there is a longer piece of ruler hanging over the edge of the table, the pitch sounds higher. ☐

It doesn't matter how much of the ruler is hanging over the edge of the table because the pitch always sounds the same. ☐

When there is a shorter length of ruler hanging over the edge of the table, the pitch sounds higher. ☐

● Think about the true statement. Can you explain why it is true? Write your explanation on the back of this sheet.

Dear Helper,

In class, your child has been learning about sound. In this activity, they use their knowledge to make predictions about sounds around them. Encourage your child to measure accurately, and to repeat the experiment as many times as they need to in order to be sure of their results.

Cool vibes!

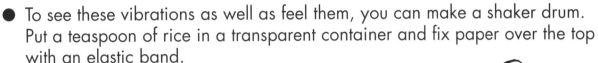

You will need: any transparent container (jam jars
are ideal), paper, an elastic band, rice, a teaspoon.

● When you blow a loud raspberry, you can feel the
vibrations on your lips. Try it!

● Now blow a quieter raspberry. What do you notice
about the vibrations this time? Were they more or less
than the last time?

● To see these vibrations as well as feel them, you can make a shaker drum.
Put a teaspoon of rice in a transparent container and fix paper over the top
with an elastic band.

● Tap the paper gently with the spoon. On the back of this sheet, describe how
loud the sound was and what happened to the rice.

● What do you think will happen if you tap the paper a bit harder? Underline
the predictions you agree with below and cross out the others.

The volume will **increase / decrease / stay the same**.

The vibration will make the rice jump **higher** than before /

jump **less** than before / jump the **same** as before / **not** jump at all.

● Now try tapping the drum harder. Record what happens on the back of this
sheet. How does it compare with your predictions?

● Try tapping the drum harder and softer as many times as you like. What
connection can you make between the sound volume and the vibration?
Write a conclusion about this on the back of the sheet.

Dear Helper,

In class, your child has been learning about how sounds are made. In this activity, they will predict and
then find out how changing a sound affects the vibrations they can see. Encourage your child to talk
through their conclusion with you and explain how they reached it.

The sound of poetry

SPONSORED POETRY-A-THON

Kate isn't very good at writing poems. She had to write an acrostic poem about sound for a sponsored Poetry-a-Thon at school. She had a wordbank, but she didn't really use it. Her poem is called 'Volume', and her friend John doesn't think it's very good either.

Very often much too high
Or so my Dad is moaning,
Listening to my music's pointless
Unless it's right up loud...
Maybe I should buy him
Ear plugs!

SOUND WORDBANK

vibration	chime	echo	hear
sound waves		tune	pluck
twang	volume	shout	note
whisper	pitch	listen	

Kate's teacher thinks that her poem has some good ideas, but that she could do better. Can you help?

● Use Kate's Sound Wordbank to help you write a new poem called 'Sounds Surround Me'. If you are not sure what some of the words mean, use a dictionary to help you. You can try different verses on the back of this sheet, then write your final draft here.

S
O
U
N
D
S

S
U
R
R
O
U
N
D

M
E

Dear Helper,

In class, your child has been learning about how we hear sounds. This activity will help them to link this knowledge to the writing skills they have developed in literacy lessons. Encourage them to draft and redraft their poem until they are happy that it is the best work they can do.